TO: Becky

you

awesome. May the Lord
continue to bless you
both. We look forward
to getting to know you
better.

Lots of Love
Angie. Cecil
Rellephart

Giant Hero

*One couple's journey through loving
and letting go of a son with
Potter's Syndrome.*

Told by Angie and Cecil Bellephant
Written by Tracy Ahrens
Funded by the University of Iowa
Potter's Syndrome Research Group

ISBN 0-7414-4948-X

Published by:

INFINITY
PUBLISHING.COM

1094 New DeHaven Street, Suite 100
West Conshohocken, PA 19428-2713
Info@buybooksontheweb.com
www.buybooksontheweb.com
Toll-free (877) BUY BOOK
Local Phone (610) 941-9999
Fax (610) 941-9959

Printed in the United States of America
Printed on Recycled Paper
Published September 2008

"This book is dedicated to Naina Batish, M.D. When Titus was born, Dr. Batish didn't give up on him. She believed. She stood by us when no one else did. She gave us time with Titus. She gave us hope. The day Titus was born, Dr. Batish was a true angel sent from God. "

- Angie Bellephant

"Thank you, Dr. Batish, for believing in our son when there was no earthly hope."

- Cecil Bellephant

A special thank you also goes to those who helped us combine important information for this book. Those people include Jason Clarke, Maren Jensen, Karen Kavanaugh and Michele Scheben-Samuel. Also, thank you to Cora Weisenberger for editing the manuscript.

Outline

Section II: Information, Resources & Inspiration

"I didn't want people to feel alone like I felt alone."
- Angie Bellephant

Introduction

I still remember the first afternoon that Angie Bellephant called me. A journalist and health editor at a daily newspaper, I was sitting at my desk when her call was routed to me.

Angie asked me through tears, "Have you ever heard of Potter's Syndrome?"

In my 11 years of health-related writing, I had not. She went on to explain that her unborn son had just been diagnosed with this condition, meaning he had no kidneys and would either be stillborn or die shortly after he was born. Potter's Syndrome is a generalized term for Bilateral Renal Agenesis.

Angie primarily was searching for answers, any information she could find to help her and her husband, Cecil, learn more about this condition and what they could do to help their son. A newspaper story may attract other readers who had been touched by the condition, she said. Maybe someone would help the Bellephants find a medical specialist who could possibly help save their son's life.

We immediately scheduled an appointment so I could meet with Angie at her home. Angie was five months pregnant and barely showed signs of it. In the womb, the fetus floats in amniotic fluid. During pregnancy the amniotic fluid increases in volume as the fetus grows, making a mother's abdomen expand outward. The baby circulates this fluid by swallowing and inhaling it. It is replaced through exhalation and urination. Because Potter's babies do not have kidneys, they do not urinate. Therefore, the womb is nearly void of amniotic fluid, causing moms to not show much outward growth.

My story about Angie was published in the newspaper and it helped her network with two area moms who also had children with Potter's.

Aside from brief meetings with those moms, Angie and Cecil still searched for information on Potter's. They found no publications about Potter's in bookstores, little information online and received just a couple sheets of information about Potter's from health care professionals.

Angie told Cecil, "No matter what happens, we have to do something. We have to write a book."

Their newspaper story touched countless readers. Strangers recognized Angie's face from a photograph that was printed with the story. They stopped her in public places and shared words of faith, advice and hugs.

The outcome of her birth was bittersweet. Titus was born in Angie's eighth month of pregnancy. He was 3 ½ pounds, 18 inches long and died 15 hours and 7 minutes later.

We ran an updated story in the local newspaper so readers knew the outcome of Angie's birth. I then attended Titus' wake and shared my condolences with the Bellephant family. I was among at least 400 people who came that evening to also share their condolences. The funeral gathered 200 mourners with a memorable procession of vehicles that wound through town as Titus was taken to a local cemetery.

From that point on, Angie and I never forgot each other. Angie and Cecil had one son, Cyrus, who was 3 at the time Titus was born. Though odds were high that they could have another child with Potter's Syndrome, the Bellephants still wanted to have more children.

Just over a year after Titus was born, the couple went on to have another child, a girl named Genesus. She was Potter's free.

One year later, they had another girl, Joyous. She, too, was Potter's free.

Nearly four years after Titus died, Angie and I crossed paths at a local store. She had both girls with her and I was amazed at how fast they had grown. Angie and I sat in her van in the parking lot for a short time and talked about what our lives had presented us over the last few years.

Angie told me "God led me to you today."

I was curious why she said this. She told me she had been speaking to classes of undergraduate nursing students at the University of Illinois at Chicago about Titus and Potter's Syndrome. She believed that she was called by God to write a book about Titus, and she wanted me to write it for her. She told me, "I feel comfortable with you because you know my story."

I was honored by her faith in me, trusting me to tell her story so she can help others who face the diagnosis of Potter's Syndrome.

Angie told me, she felt extremely "alone" when she was told her son had Potter's.

"I told Cecil, no matter what happens, we have to do something to bring awareness to people," Angie said. "I didn't want people to feel alone like I felt alone."

We pray that this book brings comfort and hope to everyone touched by Potter's Syndrome, including parents, siblings, family members and friends. We hope it educates health care professionals on what it may be like for moms, dads and family members who face this devastating diagnosis. And, we hope it provides a doorway to obtain more information about this condition.

Section I

**Expecting, Carrying &
Saying Goodbye to Titus**

"Technically, we have had four children. You look at our family pictures and you know in your heart that there is someone missing (Titus) and that will be true forever."
- Angie Bellephant

Chapter 1

Looking back Angie Bellephant smiles when she thinks about how many children she and her husband, Cecil, originally discussed having. They were married Oct. 18, 1997; she was 20 and he was 21.

"We wanted to have two children," Angie said. "Two boys, a boy and a girl, two girls – whatever."

Actually, Angie is blessed to have any children at all based on her medical history. Before her first child, Cyrus, was born, she endured six miscarriages. She admits that she had lost all hope in having a family of her own.

Diagnosed with endometriosis, Angie was scheduled to have a hysterectomy in November of 1998. With endometriosis, the tissue that lines the uterus is found in other areas of the body in the form of lesions or tumors. These tumors can cause pain and infertility. Two weeks before her hysterectomy was scheduled to take place, Angie learned she was pregnant with Cyrus. Cyrus was born Aug. 17, 1999.

Angie recalls one miscarriage she had prior to Cyrus. She carried that baby three months. During an ultrasound examination, she was told the fetus had stopped developing. The condition is called blighted ovum or anembryonic pregnancy. In sum, a blighted ovum is when normal conception, implantation and growth of the placenta happen but no fetus develops. A blighted ovum always ends in a miscarriage within the first trimester. With a blighted ovum the body can detect that something is wrong with the fertilized egg and therefore stops developing it. It is the body's way of ensuring a woman has a healthy pregnancy and baby.

Angie went home after that ultrasound examination and that evening, around 2 a.m., she started discharging blood vaginally. She was rushed to a local hospital for a D&C. That was in August of 1998.

"I don't remember that night. I have blacked it all out of my mind," Angie said. "It wasn't really a baby. The fetus hadn't even formed."

Angie was told to wait one year after this miscarriage before trying to conceive again. But she and Cecil decided to put their future in God's hands. "We told each other, 'Whatever happens will happen,'" Angie said.

Cyrus

Just three months after her D&C, Angie was feeling sick and took a pregnancy test. She discovered the test was positive.

Her pregnancy with Cyrus was "fine, for the most part," she said. But delivering him was very difficult. She had unknowingly been losing amniotic fluid for three weeks before Cyrus was born.

"My due date with Cyrus was August 17, but I started losing fluid the third week of July," Angie said. She was working at the time and was concerned about the fluid discharge. Her physician told her that she was probably just experiencing urinary incontinence.

Angie said the discharged fluid was tested and she was told that she had a staph infection. "They told me the fluid wasn't coming from my womb," Angie said. "I had lost my mucous plug too and I knew it, but they wouldn't believe me."

Angie remembers going to lunch one afternoon with a cousin and eating something simple like peanut butter and jelly sandwiches. She visited her mom after that and remembers her mom telling her, "You look awful."

Angie said she gained 65 pounds while carrying Cyrus. "I think it was all water weight," she said.

When she left her mom's house that afternoon, she thought, "I'm having this kid."

Angie went home and then to a hospital, alone. A nurse told Angie that she was probably just in false labor. So, Angie called Cecil at work and told him to just continue working his shift.

She said her obstetrician/gynecologist was frustrated that she was at the hospital again thinking that her baby should be delivered, so they made her walk the hospital halls for an hour while wearing an absorbent pad. The medical staff wanted to gather some of the fluid that Angie said she was losing.

"Sure enough, they tested the fluid again and said it was coming from my womb," Angie said.

"I told the nurses, 'You have to take him out now or he's going to die.' Something in me kept telling me I had to be persistent. My motherly instinct kicked in."

Angie said she has no idea how Cyrus survived. She experienced a "dry birth" with Cyrus, meaning little amniotic fluid was left to help him exit the birth canal. She noted that the delivery was very painful and she probably should have delivered him by caesarean section.

"Cyrus should have been in respiratory distress, but he made it," Angie said. "It's amazing to me that he's here. He could have suffocated or developed a staph infection."

Titus

It was June of 2002 when Angie and Cecil learned they were pregnant with Titus.

"I remember my grandmother had died around the time we found out I was pregnant," Angie said. "It was nice because new life was coming when grandma had gone away."

Angie said she had a feeling, however, early in her pregnancy that something was "wrong" with her son.

"Actually, the day I took the pregnancy test and found out it was positive, I told myself 'What's the point? I'm just going to lose this baby.' I just had this feeling inside," Angie said.

When she reached her third month of pregnancy her fears started to intensify. She was wearing white pants one day, looked down and saw that she was bleeding vaginally.

"I went home and took a bath," Angie said. "I put my pants in a bag to show the doctor when I saw her that afternoon. The doctor looked at my pants and said, 'The baby is probably gone.'"

However, when her doctor performed an ultrasound check of the womb, there were clear signs of a heartbeat and Titus was actively moving.

"I thought to myself, 'This is a sick joke.' I had passed blood clots the size of my fist that day," Angie said. "Some people told me that maybe I was pregnant with twins and lost one that day. I do not know."

Angie carried on, she said, praying often, "Please Lord, don't let me lose this baby. Whatever I need to do, let me keep him."

Angie's physician told her that maybe she had lifted something too heavy and it caused her to bleed that day. No further medical tests were performed. "I told myself that I probably panicked for nothing," Angie said.

"Sometimes now I look back at that prayer I said and wonder, maybe I shouldn't have prayed to God to let me keep him. Maybe God was trying to take Titus and not let me go through all of this. You have to be careful for what you pray for because you can get what you pray for. I got to continue carrying him and deliver him, but I did not get to keep him forever. But I am honored that I was able to hold my son after he was born."

On November 11 during a level two ultrasound, Angie and Cecil were told that Titus had no kidneys and would die.

Titus was born Feb. 3, 2003 during Angie's eighth month of pregnancy. He was 3 ½ pounds, 18 inches long and died 15 hours and 7 minutes later.

Family members and friends told Angie and Cecil that they should not try to have more children. Her obstetrician/gynecologist even said that after having a baby with Potter's Syndrome, she wouldn't take the risk and try to have another child.

Once you have a Potter's baby, the risk of carrying a fetus with some kind of kidney defect is about three percent, according to information posted by the International Potter's Syndrome Support Family. But in the vast majority of cases, Potter's Syndrome is an isolated abnormality and will not recur in the same family.

Angie and Cecil put their faith in God to decide.

Genesus and Joyous

For the next two years Angie was pregnant – first with Genesus who was born April 29, 2004 and then with Joyous who was born June 19, 2005.

"Genesus was planned," Angie said, "but Joyous, well, she was a surprise. Someone at church told me one day 'You're pregnant.' That same night Cyrus came up to me and told me he was praying that I'd have a baby. I took a pregnancy test and sure enough, I was pregnant.

"I would like to have one more child," Angie said. "I would like one more child because I'd like a boy. It's not that I would name him Titus, and he wouldn't replace Titus, but I want to give Cyrus a brother. That means a lot to me. He really wants a brother and we'd also have an even number of children.

"Technically, we have had four children," Angie said, noting that Titus is always with them in spirit. "You look at our family pictures and you know in your heart that there is someone missing (Titus) and that will be true forever."

"I knew his name was going to be Titus."
- Angie Bellephant

Chapter 2

All four of the Bellephant children were named for spiritual reasons, evidence of the family's strong faith in God.

Cyrus, their first child, is named after King Cyrus (born c. 600 BC). Cyrus conquered Babylon at the time many Israelites had been exiled there. He allowed the Jews to return to their native land.

Cyrus was also referred to as God's anointed, which can also be translated as "God's son" or "anointed builder." This is shown in Psalm 1 where God's anointed King is called his son. God had a special relationship with Cyrus. God anointed him with power to help the people of God. (Isaiah 44:24-45:7)

According to historical sources, Cyrus is remembered as being even-handed, humane and respectful of indigenous cultures and religions. Modern scholars sometimes credit him as being the founder of multiculturalism.

To carry on family tradition, Angie and Cecil gave Cyrus the middle name of Vance, Cecil's grandfather's first name.

The evening after the Bellephants learned that they were expecting a second son, the name Titus came to Angie.

Their first ultrasound (at about five months gestation) revealed reason for concern for the Bellephants. It did not provide a clear image as most ultrasounds do. Angie only knew she had a low level of amniotic fluid in the womb. She went home from the hospital that evening and prayed.

"I was sitting in a chair with my Bible in my hands," Angie said. "I said 'I don't know what is going on God, but please give me a sign.' I opened the Bible and it came to the chapter of Titus. I said 'Titus.' I knew his name was going to be Titus. His middle name was Franklin, after my dad's first name."

Titus, as it reads on their son's grave marker, means "giant hero, free man."

In the New Testament, Titus was a companion of Paul of Tarsus, mentioned in several of Paul's epistles, including the Epistle to Titus.

Other meanings for the name Titus include "title of honor" and "defender."

Cyrus pointed out to Angie one day that his name and Titus' name both end in "us." In other words, "Us." That symbolism was powerful for Angie.

Just over a year after Titus was born Angie had a third child named Genesus.

"After losing Titus, I didn't think I could get pregnant again," Angie said. "I was lucky. I thought, it is up to the Lord if he wants us to have another child."

When Angie and Cecil learned they were expecting their third child, they found themselves dancing in their living room with Cyrus, rejoicing and praising God. Again, a name came to Angie – Genesus.

Derived from the word genesis, meaning beginning, Angie changed the "is" in their daughter's name to "us."

"Cecil and I then chose Hope for her middle name, because after the loss of Titus, Genesus brought us hope." Angie said.

Just over a year later, the Bellephant's fourth child was born.

"We were all worshipping at home again as a family and I had the name Joyous come to me," Angie said. "We decided that if we had another girl we'd name her Joyous Faith. Cecil loved that name."

"Cecil and I knew that our only option was to carry Titus as far as we could. Doctors could not tell me Titus was suffering. I would never let any of my children suffer. Titus was alive. Very much alive."
- Angie Bellephant

Chapter 3

In June of 2002 Angie and Cecil learned they were pregnant with Titus.

Roughly three months into her pregnancy Angie started bleeding vaginally, but after an ultrasound check, she was told her baby's heart was still beating and he was moving actively inside of the womb.

Despite being told Titus was fine, Angie said she still had an instinctual, "deep-rooted, aching" feeling something was wrong with her son.

"I remember being at work one day and tracking my pregnancy week by week on the Internet, and the things I felt and the way I looked were not adding up," Angie said. "I wasn't getting very big and I thought that was weird. And I should have felt him kick and move but I was barely feeling him. I kept asking my doctor about these things but the ultrasound revealed a heartbeat. So then I started thinking that maybe with this pregnancy I was just going to be smaller. I continued to try to tell myself 'Just enjoy this pregnancy.'

"I asked my doctor one day, 'Why do I have this incredible fear?'" Angie said. "My doctor told me that I hadn't been pregnant in three years and some women just feel this fear."

On November 7 Angie had an ultrasound to determine if her child was a boy or a girl. The morning of that ultrasound, Angie said Titus kicked her inside of the womb; this was the first time she felt him move during her pregnancy. But during the ultrasound, the radiographer could not see details of her son on the screen.

"Usually fluid in the womb allows the ultrasound waves to bounce off your baby and show details of the child, but I had little fluid in the womb," Angie said.

Angie said she could see her son's face, but others who looked at the images could not discern details. Angie and Cecil were told that day that their baby was a boy.

Angie knew from the image seen on the screen that something was wrong. With her son Cyrus, the ultrasound image was clear at this stage in her pregnancy. But with Titus, it was not.

"I asked the radiographer what was wrong and the radiographer asked me back, 'What do you mean what's wrong?' I could see my son moving, but there were no details in the image."

The radiographer asked her if she had been losing amniotic fluid. Angie said, "No."

That day Angie and Cecil were also told that their unborn son had kidneys, Angie said; the radiographer said that kidneys were seen on the screen.

"This is where a lot of our pain comes in," Angie said. "Many people didn't understand the confusion we were going through. I don't remember seeing these things on the screen, but Cecil said he saw the kidneys, bladder and so on."

That day she was told to go home, drink plenty of fluid and put her feet up and rest, Angie said. "No one would tell me why I couldn't see my baby clearly on the ultrasound.

"When I got home I was distraught. I knew something was wrong. You couldn't see him on the ultrasound. You should be able to see a baby sucking his thumb. But this was like looking at a black and white picture and trying to make out an image."

Angie called her family doctor that afternoon and asked her doctor if results of the ultrasound were received. "My family doctor asked me, 'They didn't tell you anything?' No. No one was telling me anything. I only knew that I had a low amniotic fluid level."

That day Angie started to drink water, "tons of water," she said. "I didn't know what to do but drink water."

Angie started searching the Internet for information about "low amniotic fluid" during pregnancy and read that sometimes a baby will have malformed or no kidneys. But, she said, "I remember the radiographer told us that our baby had kidneys seen on that ultrasound."

That evening her family doctor told her that a level 2 ultrasound was scheduled for Monday, November 11 at the University of Chicago Medical Center. During a level 2 ultrasound, or ultrasound anatomy scan, a baby is measured in various areas of its body. Many organs are examined, including the heart and kidneys, and amniotic fluid levels are evaluated. This type of ultrasound shows if the baby is growing appropriately and if there are any potential health problems.

"The Sunday before my level 2 ultrasound everyone at church was praying that I receive 'more fluid' for our baby," Angie said. "We weren't praying for kidneys for our son because at that point we thought he had them."

Angie remembers seeing Titus on the level 2 ultrasound at the University of Chicago Medical Center. "I thought 'Yeah! He was there!'" she said. But then the room seemed very dark.

"The radiologist finished the exam, put the ultrasound wand down and held my hand," Angie said. "He told us, 'I'm so sorry, but your son has no kidneys and he will die.' It took less than 20 minutes for the exam. I immediately asked him to check again.

"During my first ultrasound, the radiographer told us that Titus had kidneys," Angie said. "But from what I have learned since then, you could be on the job (as a radiographer) 25 years and only see one case of a child with Potter's. I don't blame that radiographer. That person is still sad for the misdiagnosis that day."

Angie and Cecil were told after the level 2 ultrasound that Titus had one kidney but it had stopped growing, probably at 10 weeks. At 10 weeks of development in the womb, a baby's kidney function usually kicks in on its own. The fetal kidneys are responsible for the production of amniotic fluid in the womb. In the womb, the baby inhales the fluid into its lungs and this causes the lungs to grow. When the kidneys are absent or not working, amniotic fluid is not produced and the lungs cannot develop properly. As a result, when the baby is born it is unable to breathe properly.

After visiting with the radiologist, Angie and Cecil were asked to speak with a perinatologist. I remember his words, Angie said, "If you think you are crying now, wait until you leave the hospital with nothing." He then told them, Angie said, that they had two weeks remaining to have an elective abortion according to Illinois law.

"I told him, 'You're goofy. We aren't doing that,'" Angie said.

Angie recalled their drive home from the hospital that day.

"I remember I wanted to punch the windows out of the car," Angie said. "We had a Grand Am. I was hot and nauseous. I wanted to kill myself, just take the wheel from Cecil and bash it into my stomach and not live anymore. But then I thought about Cyrus. Then I thought, 'Maybe the doctors are wrong? It was just a machine taking an X-ray.'"

During the ride home, no words were shared between Cecil and Angie. The radio was off. Only tears were shed. "I did say a few choice words to God," Angie said.

"Titus was moving on the ultrasound that day. He was moving a lot," Angie said. "Cecil and I knew that our only option was to carry Titus as far as we could. Doctors could not tell me Titus was suffering. I would never let any of my children suffer. Titus was alive. Very much alive."

Why did Angie and Cecil decide to continue carrying Titus? Angie said the reasons were different for both of them.

"For Cecil it was because of his faith," she said. "We are both pro-life. But at the time, Cecil's faith was more deeply rooted than mine.

"For me, it was also because of the 'mothering' instinct in me. I thought 'What kind of mother would I be to just throw Titus away like that?' I wanted to at least see him and hold him. Yes, it was possible he could die in the womb. But it was possible he would also be born alive. I wanted to have the chance to touch him while he was alive."

Angie also recalls a dream she had while carrying Titus. In this dream, God was a huge figure and Titus was a tiny baby. "I had this vision in my head that Titus asked God, 'Please let me be with my mom.' But God said, 'No.' And Titus asked Him again, 'Even if for a little while?' That is what I believe God allowed him to do. God granted Titus time to be with me."

boy

04 Dec 02
11:30:40 am

What a day.
a boy. ☺ mom
it. Daddy thou
were a girl. S
Your name wi

This ultrasound image taken in December 2002 shows Titus in the womb. Angie's first ultrasound was November 7. At that time, Angie and Cecil learned their child would be a boy. The morning of that ultrasound, Angie said Titus kicked her inside of the womb; that was the first time she felt him move during her pregnancy.

"We just did the best we knew how to do. I endured as much as I could. I didn't want to give up on Titus. I would tell Titus this every day. But I was so tired."
- Angie Bellephant

Chapter 4

After Angie and Cecil learned that Titus had Potter's Syndrome, Angie channeled her efforts into finding all information possible about this condition.

"I thought, there had to be someone else out there whose child had this condition and could help me," Angie said.

One step she took was contacting a local newspaper to see if they would write a feature story about Potter's Syndrome. She achieved that goal with a story published the week before Thanksgiving 2002. This story, Angie said, would at least spread the word about Potter's.

Online she found limited information about Potter's, Angie said, but one Web site, a support group for Potter's moms called International Potter's Syndrome Support Family, became a lifeline for her.

Not having a computer at home, Angie used one at a local library and routinely shared e-mail with other Potter's moms. She learned of one mother of a Potter's baby who lived in the same area. This lady's baby was delivered shortly after diagnosis. "Her baby was very small, just over one pound," Angie said.

A second mom who lost a child to Potter's also contacted Angie from the same area. "This lady carried her child 30 weeks and then had a caesarean section. Both of these ladies reached out to me as much as they could. I met them both in person, but then our communication ended.

"The Potter's moms here in my town did not want to talk too much about the past," Angie said. "They didn't understand why I asked the local newspaper to write a story. I also shared the idea with these moms about writing a book some day about Potter's. I wanted to write a book because the first few hours after you are diagnosed, you look for information and there is nothing available. I am a need-to-know kind of person. However, many people accept things for the way they are and they go on. Many people want things to just go away. Some people like to grieve privately. I'm am not like that. I will talk about Titus to anyone.

"I also knew that we have to find a cure some day for this condition," Angie said. "There has to be a cure."

Soon, Angie obtained a computer to use at home on a more frequent basis. "Women would talk to me online about our symptoms and such," she said. "This Web site (International Potter's Syndrome Support Family) was my main source of information and help at that time."

Members of her church continued to pray for Angie and Cecil and placed them on a prayer chain for spiritual support.

While Angie scoured every source she could find for information about Potter's, she often faced negative comments from family members, friends and strangers about her decision to carry Titus.

"When we shared Titus' diagnosis with our family and friends, many of them told me to be 'induced,' which is basically having an abortion," Angie said. "When we told them we wouldn't induce early, people thought we were nuts. I had one friend tell me that if she went through this, she would lock herself in her bedroom and never come out. She would be angry with God, her husband and everyone."

In her heart, Angie said she knew Titus would not live a full life, or come home with them after he was born. "But I knew he would make it long enough for us to be with him," she said.

Possibly the worst part of her pregnancy was the physical pain she quietly endured.

"I didn't think the pregnancy would be painful," Angie said. "Sometimes I think about the pain I had and how I didn't tell anyone how I was feeling. I never told my friends or my mom, but Cecil knew. I didn't tell people because so many people were judgmental of me. Some people were telling me that I was 'so strong.' I couldn't tell anyone about my physical pain. I felt like people wanted to see me fail. I didn't want them to see me fail."

Because Angie had very little amniotic fluid in the womb, there was little room for Titus to move. When he did a somersault or kicked, "It was like bone rubbing on bone," Angie said.

"Doctors didn't tell me about the pain involved in carrying a child with little amniotic fluid," Angie said. "When I told doctors about my pain, they looked at me like I was coo-coo. Carrying him with little fluid was a mentally grueling process. When he kicked I felt excruciating pain. There were days when I wished I had drugs for the pain, but I knew those drugs could hurt Titus."

Angie had many moments where she questioned her faith and voiced her anger at God.

"For the longest time I thought, 'How cruel can God be to allow this to happen to someone?' I was angry with Him, but I knew there is a God and I guess … the thing I remember asking God often was 'Why me?' One night I thought about that question and told myself, 'Why *not* me?' That answer got me through when I was feeling anger and sadness that Titus was going to die. I would say 'Why not me?' and I would tell myself that there are many children who live but face many surgeries or live in a persistent vegetative state. At least my son wasn't going to hurt. 'Why not me?' I put this quote on like armor and people would look at me when I responded this way as if I had lost my mind.

"I believed that Titus had a right to live some type of a life. I stand up for what I believe in. I was hurting physically, but I knew that Titus was not suffering. I would never have carried him if I knew he was hurting, if he was suffering inside of me. He was completely happy inside of my belly. He kicked and had hiccups like a normal baby. For the most part, it was a normal pregnancy."

While Angie faced opinions from family members and friends, she also faced opinions from her husband. Not all were accepted.

"There were times I wanted a divorce," Angie said. "I was done with Cecil and his opinions on how I should deal with things and how I should act. I thought, 'Who are you and who gives you the right?'

"I felt like everyone wanted me to break," she said. "I remember that some people asked if I was 'on medication yet' to deal with the pregnancy and losing my son. What most people didn't realize about me is that when I am told I will fail, I prove them wrong.

"Yes, I did want to crawl under a rock and die. I actually wanted to kill myself at times. Many people told me 'Be thankful you have your son Cyrus.' At that time I was not thinking about Cyrus much, I was thinking about myself and how angry I was. I still had to be around other pregnant women who were having healthy babies and I couldn't have mine. You get angry. You get *very* angry with different people. You keep trying to cope in the best ways you know how."

Angie also contacted local radio stations and asked if prayers could be said for her son.

"It wasn't about bringing attention to myself, I was crying out for help. I didn't know what to do," Angie said. "I would have laid down my life for that baby. I asked God many times to spare Titus' life and take mine instead."

Some people shared scripture with Angie, believing that faith would make Titus live.

"I didn't want to read the Bible," Angie said. "I tried to, but in my mind, in my heart, I thought that if God was such a happy God, why would he allow this to happen to me and my son?"

Angie also avoided being around "happy people" during her pregnancy. "We had many people tell us things like, 'Your baby is going to live!' And the first reaction in my mind was, 'Are you God? No, you aren't, so don't say these things to me.'"

With every piece of advice they received verbally or through print, Angie and Cecil acted quickly to try to save their son. "We were running out to the store at midnight to buy certain vitamins because someone wrote us a letter and said that a certain vitamin could help our child produce stronger lungs," Angie said. "We just did the best we knew how to do. I endured as much as I could. I didn't want to give up on Titus. I would tell Titus this every day. But I was so tired.

"Things became very chaotic for us when one person told us one thing and another would tell us to do another thing," Angie said. "You start to feel like 'If I do this, will this person get mad?' I didn't want anyone to hurt with me. People asked me often 'How do you do it?' I told them, 'I don't know. I'm a mother. When you are a mother, you just do it.'"

"I think that God dealt with me first to accept Titus' fate. Because, if I had believed strongly like Cecil did that Titus was going to live, and then he died, I probably wouldn't be here right now."
- Angie Bellephant

Chapter 5

The days immediately after Titus was diagnosed with Potter's were like living in a fog, Angie said.

"I was asked to see my doctor more frequently to keep monitoring Titus' development, in case he died in the womb," Angie said. At first she went once a week, but then she stopped going so frequently.

"I was having ultrasounds every two weeks, but eventually it got to me," Angie said. "I couldn't do it anymore. I was seeing my son over and over on the screen and his status was not changing. It would have been different if they were seeing more amniotic fluid or something, but things were the same. He was growing, but not very good.

"I didn't think the pregnancy would be painful," Angie said. "Doctors didn't tell me about the pain involved in carrying a child with little amniotic fluid.

"One day I was doing dishes at home and Titus moved, he did a somersault," Angie said. "I remember reaching out to grab something and I grabbed the kitchen counter. I was home alone and I remember the pain took my breath away. Cecil and Cyrus were out for a bike ride at the time."

While Angie wanted Titus to move inside of her womb, showing her that he was alive, she was fearful of the pain. "Often three days or more would pass between his movements," Angie said. "Normally babies move all the time. Women start to feel their baby move a lot between 14 and 20 weeks of development. When Titus didn't move, I feared he was dead.

"I didn't gain much weight while carrying Titus either," Angie said. "Most weight gain while you are pregnant is water weight."

Early on, Angie started drinking extra water hoping it would help produce more amniotic fluid for Titus in the womb. She stopped consuming extra water when she learned it would not change his condition.

Comments from strangers in public were difficult for Angie to answer.

"People would say to me, 'When are you due?' and I told them March 17. They looked at me, my size being so small so close to my due date, and said, 'You're awfully tiny.' I got to the point that I felt I had to tell everyone why. I told them, 'I don't have fluid and my son doesn't have kidneys,'" Angie said. "Some people would say to me, 'Well can he have a kidney transplant?' and then I'd have to go through the whole story about why that wasn't an option."

Once people read Angie's story in a local newspaper, and recognized her face from an accompanying photograph, they started to address her in public. "I remember how some people would see us in a restaurant and start to whisper and look at us," Angie said. "Some people, strangers, would come up to us and tell us they were praying for us.

"Some people tried to tell me nice things, like 'The doctors are probably wrong honey, it was just an X-ray machine.' Then Cecil would tell me, 'I told you!' Cecil didn't want to accept the diagnosis," Angie said. "Our marriage became very strained.

"I remember Cecil's uncle came over one day and started speaking negative words about the pregnancy and Cecil told him he had to leave," Angie said. "Cecil didn't want negative words in our house. He wanted us all to stay positive.

"One night Cecil and I had a heated discussion about Titus," Angie said. "Cecil told me, 'He's going to live and that's the final word!' I told him, 'He's not going to live Cecil. He's going to die.' He told me I was hearing from the devil and that I was wrong. At that time we both sat down and prayed. Cecil was in the living room praying and I was in the bedroom praying. Then we came together and Cecil told me once again, 'God told me that Titus is going to live.' I told Cecil, 'God told me he's going to die. He can't be telling both of us the wrong thing.'

"Cecil still didn't want to hear me. He remembers that I said to him, 'Did God tell you how long Titus will live?' Cecil told me, 'No.' And this was the eerie part, I asked Cecil, 'Did God tell you he would he would live, like 15 hours or something?' Titus ended up living 15 hours and 7 minutes. God did let Titus live and then took him away. At this time in the pregnancy, God had to deal with Cecil's heart more than mine.

"I think that God dealt with me first to accept Titus' fate," Angie said. "Because, if I had believed strongly like Cecil did that Titus was going to live, and then he died, I probably wouldn't be here right now. I probably would have killed myself, because when you put your faith so strongly into something and it fails, you almost have nothing to live for. I know that God knew my personality. I am a need-to-know type of person. I need to have details. I'm hands-on. If there is a will there is a way. I remember telling my dad that I would pay anything to have Titus live. But even having all the money in the world, no doctor would have been able to fix this situation. I had been hoping for a miracle.

"You have to remember that men are Band-Aids, they want to fix things and Cecil couldn't fix this situation. He was trying to be supportive. He worked midnight shifts and when he wasn't sleeping or working, he was praying. He even fasted. He believed with all his heart. It was hard because," Angie paused with tears, "because I watched him doing all this and I felt terrible. He walked in so strongly that day when we had the level 2 ultrasound. He felt there would be fluid in my womb at that time.

"I couldn't continue having ultrasounds so often," Angie said. "I knew no fluid would be there. I didn't want to be around healthy, pregnant women anymore either. It was hard for us every time to hear Titus' heartbeat. I remember being at home and thinking that I heard his heartbeat and thinking, 'He must be going to live.' But I realize now that I was the one keeping him alive."

Angie poses for a picture while she was pregnant with Titus. Since there was little amniotic fluid in the womb, Angie did not appear far along in her pregnancy. Because Angie had very little amniotic fluid, there was also little room for Titus to move. When he did, the pain was excruciating, Angie said.

"I was overcome with joy that Titus was close to being born, that I would get to see him ... But then sadness came over me. I knew that if he was born, I would not have control anymore, that he would die."
- Angie Bellephant

Chapter 6

Titus was predicted to be born March 17, 2003. Since he had Potter's Syndrome, there was a chance that he would be delivered sooner, Angie said. For Angie, the delivery came over one month early.

"I remember going to a Christian music concert with a couple of friends," Angie said. "At the concert, I remember feeling Titus jump inside of me. I think he was jumping for joy. That was a moment I will never forget. He felt the music."

That night, Angie went to a local hospital because she felt that she was in labor. "They examined me and told me I was just a fingertip dilated and so they sent me home," she said.

Around midnight, Angie woke having painful contractions. "I got up from bed and took a hot bath to feel better," Angie said. "I remember talking to Titus while I was in the tub. I was overcome with joy that Titus was close to being born, that I would get to see him. But then sadness came over me. I knew that if he was born, I would not have control anymore, that he would die. This frightened me. I had to surrender everything to God at that point."

Around 4 a.m. Angie woke Cecil and he helped ease her pain by rubbing her back. Angie eased her pain some more by doing squatting exercises.

At 6 a.m. they called the pastor of their church and told him that Titus was near being delivered. "My pastor told me not to think the worst and that the congregation would pray for us that morning," Angie said.

By 10 a.m. that day her contractions stopped and remained quiet until around 2 p.m, Angie said. "Then they suddenly started again," she said. "I told Cecil I couldn't take it anymore. I was in pain, agony, just very tired. I wanted this over with.

"I tried to be strong," Angie said. "Maybe a bit selfish because I thought in the middle of all this, 'What's the point of going to the hospital?'" She knew Titus was going to die after he was born. While he was in the womb, Angie was keeping him alive. "I also didn't want to be hooked up to monitors and stuff."

Angie and Cecil went to a nearby hospital and learned that she was dilated to 2 centimeters. Active labor usually begins when the cervix is 3 to 4 cm dilated. Since Titus was so small in the womb, Angie's obstetrician/gynecologist noted early in the pregnancy that Titus could be delivered when she was just a couple of centimeters dilated.

"It seemed like everyone (in the hospital birthing center) was nervous," Angie said. "They knew I could have Titus quickly and that he was a high-risk birth."

Angie's obstetrician/gynecologist had made the birthing center team members aware that Angie's son was a high-risk birth.

Angie also requested that her pediatrician, Naina Batish, M.D. be present when Titus was born. "Dr. Batish believed in me from the start," Angie said. "She gave me courage and hope."

"Most of the birthing center team members had been told by my obstetrician that Titus' condition was rare and that he would die after birth," Angie said. "The team was caring, compassionate and loving to us all."

During labor, Titus' heartbeat stopped twice, Angie said.

"At one point a nurse turned down the heart monitor volume so we couldn't hear it when Titus flatlined," Angie said. "I remember team members standing in one corner talking at one point and I told them, 'Please, if anything is to be said here, say it to Cecil and me.' That's when they responded with, 'He probably passed away because we haven't found his heartbeat. We can't pick it up.' I remember telling them, 'No, that's not how this is supposed to happen.'

"At that point I asked for Cecil to come stand by me and we prayed," Angie said. "Shortly after, a nurse told us, 'We have his heartbeat back on the monitor again!'"

Titus was very small, Angie said, and she barely needed to push for his delivery. He was also in the breech position.

"I barely pushed and nurses told me to 'Stop,'" Angie said. "My doctor barely had time to get her gown on and Titus came out."

Dr. Batish said that she had been asked by Angie to be present when Titus was born. Dr. Batish left instructions at the birthing center for someone to call her when Angie was ready to deliver. She was paged immediately and arrived just before Titus was born.

"I had requested to hold Titus before anyone else did," Angie said. "My doctor handed him to me and told me, 'Here is your miracle.'"

Titus entered the world at 2:48 a.m., Monday, Feb. 3, 2003. He weighed 3 ½ pounds and was 18 inches long. "He was a good size for a Potter's baby," Angie said.

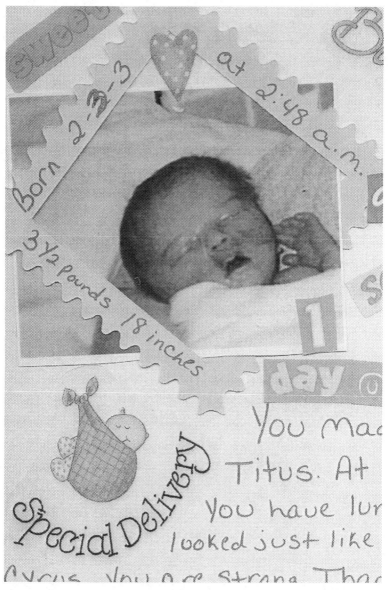

Titus Franklin Bellephant was born Feb. 3, 2003 at 2:48 a.m. He weighed 3 ½ pounds and was 18 inches long. He looked like his brother, Cyrus, Angie said.

"I finally told Titus, 'You fought a good fight.
God is waiting for you.' I told him, 'Go towards the
Light.' And then I sang to him a short, simple song that
came to my mind at that moment,
'You Are My Sunshine.'"
- Angie Bellephant

Chapter 7

Angie remembers holding her son immediately after he was born. She remembers his skin coloring, a "charcoal black," and fearing he was dead.

Dr. Batish explained that premature babies usually are born with a darker skin color. Once they receive adequate oxygen, she said, their skin turns pink in color.

"After Titus took a few breaths on his own, his skin turned more pink in color," Angie said. Titus was swept away from Angie's arms quickly by medical staff in order to tend to his health needs.

Dr. Batish said that when Titus was born, he cried. This alone was a shocking sign since medical staff knew he was a Potter's baby, a baby that had no kidneys and thus, poor lung development.

"He also didn't look like a typical Potter's baby," Dr. Batish said. She had delivered one other Potter's baby in her career.

Dr. Batish explained that a baby born to a mother with low amniotic fluid typically has dry skin and possibly a squashed-looking face or clubbed feet and hands. "This child was not a classic-looking Potter's baby," she said.

"He was pink, he had a heartbeat and he cried when he was born."

Titus had lungs, Dr. Batish said, noting that they were the size and composition of lungs a premature baby would have. She routinely administered surfactant into his lungs. Surfactant is a substance that keeps air sacs inside of the lungs from sticking together when they inflate and deflate during breathing. Premature lungs don't immediately produce this substance and the lungs can collapse.

Titus was immediately placed on a ventilator.

Dr. Batish explained that she spoke to Angie and Cecil before Titus was born. Knowing that Titus had Potter's and was expected to die quickly, she needed to know if Angie and Cecil wanted him placed on life-support or not.

A do not resuscitate (DNR) order has to be signed by both parents prior to labor, Dr. Batish said. A DNR order is a medical treatment order that says cardiopulmonary resuscitation (CPR) will not be used if the heart and/or breathing stops.

"Angie had told me, 'I need you to be there when he's born,'" Dr. Batish said. Before Angie went into labor, the family believed that Titus would have kidneys; that he would live. No DNR form was signed.

While Angie was in labor, Dr. Batish said she asked her again, "What do you want me to do?"

Angie told Dr. Batish, "'Do everything you can to help him.'"

Considering that Titus cried, he had lungs, a heartbeat and appeared to look like any other preemie, Dr. Batish proceeded to care for him like she would with other premature babies.

Angie recalls Titus "fighting" Dr. Batish while she tended to his medical needs. "He was pushing the doctor away. He was only 3-and-a-half pounds and he was pushing her away," Angie said.

Dr. Batish was amazed at Titus' appearance, his strength – the fact that he cried.

"The family believed he could be a miracle," Dr. Batish said. Despite the fact that Titus did not have kidneys, he appeared normal. "I wasn't going to stand in the way of a possible miracle."

Most of the time that Titus was being cared for, Angie could not see him, she said. "I couldn't be with him because I was so tired. I had just given birth. I couldn't feel my legs. I was numb from the epidural. I was also afraid to see Titus like that, with tubes and things coming out of him."

Cecil stayed with Titus while he was receiving care.

"Then we had to make the decision what to do next," Angie said. "And that decision was to send Titus to the neonatal intensive care unit (NICU) at the University of Chicago Medical Center. Dr. Batish had been working on Titus from 2:48 a.m. to 7 a.m. We couldn't fly Titus to Chicago by helicopter. It was foggy outside that morning and Titus' lungs were too fragile. The pressure would have collapsed his lungs. So he was transported by ambulance."

Cecil, along with Angie's parents, drove in a vehicle behind the ambulance to the University of Chicago. Angie had to stay behind.

"I had no idea how I could get up there to the University of Chicago to be with my son," Angie said. "I had to get out of that hospital. I asked my doctor to discharge me because I wanted to be with him. But my doctor said 'No.' I told the doctor, 'Yes.' We went round-and-round."

Finally Angie won the argument and her aunt and uncle drove her to Chicago.

"When I saw Titus in Chicago I was so angry," Angie said. "There were way more tubes and things in him than I ever wanted. I did not want to have to deal with turning off any life support machines."

Titus rests in the University of Chicago Medical Center neonatal intensive care unit (NICU).

Family members and friends joined Angie and Cecil at the University of Chicago to pray for Titus.

An ultrasound was done on Titus to see if any kidney development was present. A physician told Angie and Cecil that no kidneys were seen.

"I remember asking the doctor, 'What do we do?'" Angie said.

"The doctor told us that Titus could stay on life support as long as we wanted, but because he didn't have kidneys and could not get rid of waste, and he was so frail, he would swell up like a balloon and his skin would start to literally fall off," Angie said. "I looked at Cecil and told him, 'You aren't going to let my son do that. I'll kill you first.'"

Cecil still didn't accept that his son was going to die. "He told the doctor, 'You go back and look again! There are kidneys! We can pray for some kidneys!' He did not want to take 'No' for an answer," Angie said.

After Cecil passionately spoke, Angie, Cecil and medical staff all walked away from the NICU bed where Titus was resting.

"It was really weird," Angie said. "I remember that all of us walked away at the same time, and came back to the NICU at the same time, from different directions. Cecil was already there with Titus, crying. I asked Cecil what was wrong, if something had happened. Cecil looked up at me and said, 'God dealt with me and told me that love is not selfish. We have to let Titus go.'"

Angie and Cecil looked at their doctor and the doctor informed them again that Titus had no kidneys. A second ultrasound had been performed at Cecil's request.

"We said 'Okay,' and had to sign paperwork to let our son go," Angie said.

Nurses put up a partition screen around Titus' bed in the NICU so Angie and Cecil could be with their son until he died. "There were many people in the NICU," Angie said. "I know I was crying loudly because I didn't want to let him go. But I knew I had to.

"The nurses let me sit down and Cecil was next to me. They took tubes out of Titus and turned off the life support machines. That was the worst noise ever to hear the ventilator turned off. It's a beeping nose that decreases in sound. The nurses pulled tubes out of Titus' mouth. Cecil and I asked how long he would live. The nurses told us, 15 minutes to 1 hour.

Angie and Cecil hold their son Titus in the University of Chicago Medical Center NICU. At this point he had been removed from life support. They insisted on holding Titus until he passed away, unlike many parents who ask nurses to hold their babies in the final hours or minutes of life, Angie said.

"A nurse kept asking us if we wanted to let a nurse hold Titus while he passed, but we told her, 'No.' I held him. They checked his heartbeat from time to time. Titus took a gasping breath trying to breathe on his own.

"A nurse suggested that if we wanted to give Titus a bath, we could," Angie said. "I couldn't do it. Titus was so frail.

41

I was afraid. He was long and so frail looking. But Cecil stepped in and gave him a bath. We also cut some of his hair and put it in a little bag. His footprints were taken. We didn't even have clothes with us for him to wear."

Cecil gives Titus a bath in the University of Chicago Medical Center NICU. Angie was hesitant to bathe Titus because he appeared so 'frail,' she said. Cecil said he wanted to bathe his son. At this time Titus was off of life support.

Things happened quickly after Titus was removed from life support, Angie said. "I couldn't imagine him in the hospital morgue with no clothes on, so I told Cecil to please put a diaper on him. A nurse came and gave us a gown for Titus to wear and a blanket to put around him. I was so agitated because I had not even thought to bring something for him to wear. I would have had to find doll clothes because he was so small. That is something I really regret - not having clothes for him to wear when he passed away.

"I told Cecil that once Titus passed away, I wanted to leave," Angie said. "But now, I wish I would have held him longer. The staff does let you stay with your child and grieve. I felt like everyone was watching me and I couldn't grieve privately with my son. There were other parents around us who were trying to be happy while their children were on life support. I felt like we had no privacy.

"We asked our nurse why we were repeatedly asked if we wanted to keep holding Titus until he died," Angie said. "She told us that many parents just want to kiss their child and say goodbye and then a nurse holds the baby until it dies. I thought to myself, how cruel is that? That baby doesn't know your heartbeat or your voice. Cecil told the nurse, 'We are strong.'

"But I didn't feel strong," Angie said. "I don't even remember coming home that day."

Titus was alive for 2 hours after being removed from life support.

"He was fighting the whole time," Angie said. "He didn't cry. He just gasped for breath. He never opened his eyes for me, but Cecil got to see his eyes before I got there. I wish he would have opened his eyes. I never got to see those eyes."

Angie said she grew angry with Titus as he struggled to stay alive.

"I just wanted him to go," she said. "He had been so strong up to that point. I felt he was staying around for me and Cecil. I didn't want him to fight anymore. I didn't want him to be in misery anymore. Nurses told me he wasn't hurting, but then again, you can only imagine gasping for breath and what that is like.

"I finally told Titus, 'You fought a good fight. God is waiting for you.' I told him, 'Go towards the Light.' And then I sang to him a short, simple song that came to my mind at that moment, '*You Are My Sunshine*.'"

Titus died at 5:55 p.m., Feb. 3, 2003. He lived 15 hours and 7 minutes.

"I had to be strong for everyone around me. I felt like everyone was watching me and expecting me to fall."
- Angie Bellephant

Chapter 8

"I don't remember our drive home from the hospital after Titus died," Angie said. From his death to the wake and funeral, Angie and Cecil's lives were a whirlwind of planning and announcing Titus' death to friends and family.

"I remember being in the hospital elevator the day we left the NICU at the University of Chicago," Angie said. "There was someone carrying a bunch of balloons for a new baby that said 'Congratulations, it's a boy!' I wanted to pop all of those balloons."

With diminishing strength, Angie made calls to family and friends from the hospital, telling them that Titus had died. "It was very hard to call everyone and tell them we had to let him go with dignity and in peace," Angie said.

"Then I worried about how we would get his body back to our home town from the hospital, for his wake," Angie said. "I worried that they would send the wrong baby because, at first I didn't remember what he looked like. That may sound crazy, but everything happened so fast."

Titus died on a Monday. His wake was planned for Friday. His funeral was on Saturday.

"The night we came home we started making plans for his funeral," Angie said, noting they called a local funeral home that evening. "The next day we went out to purchase flowers for the wake and funeral."

Angie tried to stay focused, but she felt as though friends and family were examining her quietly. "I had to be strong for everyone around me," Angie said, "including Cecil, Cyrus, my mom and dad. I felt like everyone was watching me and expecting me to fall. I didn't sleep for several days. Our phone at home rang all the time and people kept coming to the door. My aunt asked me at one point, 'Are you sure you are okay? Do you need medication?'

"Others were telling us what to do for the funeral," Angie said. "We were bombarded with questions at the funeral home about things that were free and things that cost extra. Then we had to share information to put in the local newspaper about Titus' death.

"While we were running around making all these plans, people were kindly leaving food for us outside of our front door, but it was always ruined by the time we got back home," she said.

One choice the Bellephants made for Titus' wake was showing him in an open casket. "Some people didn't like that decision and they left the wake when they saw Titus. They couldn't handle it," Angie said.

Titus held in his hand a necklace that featured a cross-shaped pendant. Angie's mother, Connie, gave it to him.

A special item they had delivered to the wake was a concrete statue of an angel sitting in a basket. "We wanted something special delivered in Titus' honor," Angie said.

Looking back, Angie said that she would have liked to have Titus cremated, not buried.

"I would have kept some of his ashes in a necklace (locket or vial)," she said. "I would have liked to have taken the rest of his ashes and scattered them in an ocean."

Then again, Angie said, she couldn't handle the thought of her son being "burned" for cremation, either.

Titus' wake and funeral plans were all organized in one day, Angie said. She wishes there would have been more time.

"I would have put his picture on his headstone and the stone would have been larger," Angie said. "I really wanted a ledger stone."

It cost the Bellephants $60 to bury Titus, Angie said. The funeral was free, a service a local funeral home provides for those who have lost a baby. The most expensive item was Titus' headstone that cost the Bellephants $3,000.

His headstone notes a unique epitaph, a message based on the meaning of his name and his spirit: *Giant Hero/Free Man.*

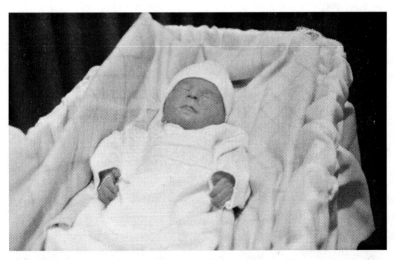

Angie and Cecil chose to show their son, Titus, in an open casket at his wake. Angie said about this image she captured at the wake, 'He looked like a baby doll.'

"Even though it was hard to let him go, I thanked God that He gave him (Titus) to us in that short amount of time so we could give him back. I thank God for that."
- Cecil Bellephant

Chapter 9

At least 200 people came to support Angie and Cecil the day Titus was laid to rest, Saturday, Feb. 8, 2003. Twice that number of people visited his wake the evening before.

At just 3 ½ pounds, Titus touched the lives of countless people and his funeral ceremony was a reflection of the love, strength and life lessons he brought into this world.

Various family members and friends shared words at his wake. Angie and Cecil recorded the funeral on audiotape and have listened to it since Titus passed. The words have helped them in their healing process.

Saturday, Feb. 8, 2003

After a family friend spoke, Angie presented a tribute for Titus.

She first read the poem *"I asked God"* that was handed out in print to everyone at the wake and funeral. Her tears made her pause many times during the eulogy.

"A month after I found out that Titus was going to die, I went to get a haircut and the lady who cut my hair said she had just gotten an e-mail and she thought I should read it," Angie said at Titus' funeral. "Cecil and I read it and thought it was beautiful. We put the piece of paper aside.

"The day that Titus passed away, Cecil and I came home from the hospital and the Lord told me to go get that poem. And I pulled it out and realized that it was written from Titus to me and Cecil."

As a line in capital letters beneath the poem read:

"To the world you might be one person, but to one person you just might be the whole world."

"That's what Titus was – the whole world," Angie said. "He gave us in his short time … he gave us love and I think we all need to start loving on each other. We never know when the moments may be gone."

She proceeded to read from a sympathy card. It contained words from a nurse that took care of Titus at the University of Chicago Medical Center:

"When someone comes into our lives and they are too quietly and quickly gone, they leave their footprints in our hearts and their memory stays with us forever."

The card continued to read …

"Titus is a fighter. He's very lucky to have such incredible love from such wonderful parents. Your strength during this rough time has truly amazed me and I'm so lucky to have spent this time with you and your beautiful baby. We now have one more angel to love and watch over us and his name is Titus. You're in my prayers and God bless you."

"This card is very special to us," Angie said, "because we learned that night that parents rarely stay with their children there (at the University of Chicago NICU). They usually leave their children with nurses to hold them until they die. Nurses kept asking Cecil and me, 'Do you want us to take him from you? We will hold him.'

"The nurses told us that 'Parents *never* stay with their children.' But Cecil and I didn't do that. Your child needs to feel your love and comfort during that time," Angie said.

"Titus lived for two hours without anything on him (life support). He didn't want to go," Angie said with tears. "He wasn't scared for himself, he was scared for Cecil and I and all of you. If he could be a fighter at 3 pounds and stand on the Word of God, then we need to stand on the Word of God because the Bible is Truth."

Cecil then stood and presented words in honor of his son.

"I had been doing good up until now," Cecil said through tears. He referred to the Bible and the book of David. He recalled the story of Shadrach, Meshack and Abednego who went before the king of Babylon. The king had built a golden image of himself and he wanted everyone to bow to that image when trumpets called. Shadrach, Meshack and Abednego refused to bow. Because they refused, they were thrown into a fiery furnace. God protected them in the fire.

"Friends kept asking us, 'If Titus doesn't live, are you going to bow? Are you going to bow before the *golden image* or are you going to stand and say 'No - my God is greater!'" Cecil said with passion in his voice.

"Shadrach, Meshack and Abednego, they said to the king, 'We aren't worried about you. Our God can save us. God will save us in the burning fire and even if he doesn't, we are *still* not going to bow before this golden image.'

"Me and Angie have been through this fire, together," Cecil said. "Titus is now where we aspire to be. I truly believe in my heart that this baby is sitting on the Father's lap, in a mansion that the Lord Jesus built for him. Sitting at a supper table as far and as long as the eyes can see, full of the fruits of life.

"Titus fought two hours without life support because he was more worried about us than he was about himself," Cecil said. "I believe that. And I was asking God, 'Why?' I asked God 'Why?' because I didn't give up on that baby, not *one time*, thinking he would not live – not *once*. Anyone who tried to tell me differently, I had an attitude about it. I don't think that was wrong; maybe it wasn't nice, but I don't think it was wrong.

"But I asked God 'Why?' and he gave me peace about it … that's when Angie came to me with the poem ('*I asked God*') we found when we came home that night (after Titus died)," Cecil said.

Cecil then shared Bible verses about peace and love that helped him through his grieving process.

1 Corinthians 12:27-31 and 1 Corinthians 13:1-13 (New International Version)

"Now you are the body of Christ, and each one of you is a part of it. And in the church God has appointed first of all apostles, second prophets, third teachers, then workers of miracles, also those having gifts of healing, those able to help others, those with gifts of administration, and those speaking in different kinds of tongues. Are all apostles? Are all prophets? Are all teachers? Do all work miracles? Do all have gifts of healing? Do all speak in tongues? Do all interpret? But eagerly desire the greater gifts. And now I will show you the most excellent way.

"If I speak in the tongues of men and of angels, but have not loved, I am only a resounding gong or a clanging cymbal. If I have the gift of prophecy and can fathom all mysteries and all knowledge, and if I have faith that can

move mountains, but not have love, I am nothing. If I give all I possess to the poor and surrender my body to the flames, but have not love, I gain nothing.

"Love is patient, love is kind. It does not envy, it does not boast, it is not proud. It is not rude, it is not self-seeking, it is not easily angered, it keeps no record of wrongs. Love does not delight in evil but rejoices with the truth. It always protects, always trusts, always hopes, always perseveres.

"Love never fails. But where there are prophecies, they will cease; where there are tongues, they will be stilled; where there is knowledge, it will pass away. For we know in part and we prophesy in part, but when perfection comes, the imperfect disappears. When I was a child, I talked like a child, thought like a child, I reasoned like a child. When I became a man, I put childish ways behind me. Now we see but a poor reflection; then we shall see face to face. Now I know in part; then I shall know fully, even as I am fully known.

"And now these three remain: faith, hope and love. But the greatest of these is love."

"You see," Cecil said, "I didn't give up on that baby not *one* time. And it says that if I have the faith that can move mountains, but have not loved, I am nothing. God showed me a lot; that faith isn't all there is. It isn't the greatest thing.

"It says here (in the Bible) that '*Love is not self-seeking.*' That said to me that love is not selfish ... and I will explain something to you," Cecil said.

"I read this chapter about love and was stuck on that passage '*Love is not self-seeking.*' The Spirit was talking to me in these words. I kept saying it to myself over and over. Repeating it. I didn't know why.

"When we were at the University of Chicago, and Angie arrived and we spent time with the baby, we kept praying Titus would be given kidneys," Cecil said. "The doctor came in and said to us that there was nothing they could do for Titus. The doctor told us that the most humane thing we could do at that time was to take him off of the ventilator and let him pass peacefully. I didn't take that too lightly.

"I started praying and saying out loud 'We are going to get some kidneys in here or something!'

"For some reason, for a short time, all the nurses left the room, the doctors left too and Angie left. That was a time that God chose to isolate me with Titus," Cecil said.

"I was sitting beside him praying and a peace came over me. A peace came over me. And the Spirit spoke to me and said, 'Love is not self-seeking.' Because, even if Titus did have kidneys, he would have had many surgeries to fix other things that were wrong with him. And the words 'Love is not self-seeking' kept ringing in my spirit.

"Me and Angie could have made the decision to keep Titus on a ventilator, but that would have been for our own selfish reasons, to keep him here with us for a time. But in that one moment, I really got confronted with a question to myself, 'Do I truly believe that?' I do. And, I did then. Even though it was hard to let him go, I thanked God that He gave him to us in that short amount of time so we could give him back. I thank God for that.

"Now, concerning the poem 'I asked God,'" Cecil said. "In that poem it says, I asked God to give me riches and He said 'No.' And I asked God to heal my son, but God said 'No.' And in the Bible, in the love chapter, God says the same thing … if you speak in the tongues of angels, that's great, but that's not it. God said, if you have faith that can move mountains, that's good, but that's not it. If you give all your money away, if you love poor people with all your heart, you give it all up for God – *that's* not it. And the poem says, 'Lord, give me love so that I can love others,' and the Lord said 'Ahhhh … now you got it!'

"Love is patient, love is kind … now you are getting the point," Cecil said.

Cecil continued sharing scripture from Mathew 22 (New International Version)

"A Pharisee who was an expert in the law tested Jesus with this question: 'Teacher, which is the greatest commandment in the law?' Jesus replied to him, '*Love the Lord your God with all your heart and all your soul and all your mind.' And the second greatest commandment is 'Love your neighbor as yourself. All the Law and the prophets hang on these two commandments.'*

"This was a defining moment (letting Titus go)," Cecil said. "People were there who gave up their time and sleep to come and pray for the life of that little infant.

"*Love your neighbor as yourself,*" Cecil quoted scripture again. "*All the Law and the Prophets hang on these two commandments.*

"We did everything we could, but it wasn't God's Will. It says in the Bible that God's ways are past finding out. We may never know until we get to heaven with Titus to know why God did what He did. But as I said earlier, me and Angie were not going to bow before the golden idol. We were going through this situation, this trial to get it behind us and to push us into a new life together - a new purpose for our life."

"(Cyrus) has endured way more than any child should have at his age. He tells things like they are. His feelings are real and he is very softhearted. We allow him to express how he feels about Titus."
- Angie Bellephant

Chapter 10

From the day that Titus was diagnosed with Potter's Syndrome, Angie and Cecil never hid the truth about his condition from their son Cyrus. Cyrus was 3 at the time.

"The day Titus died, we came home and told Cyrus that God took Titus home," Angie said. "We were very honest with him."

Angie recalled the night she and Cecil came home from the University of Chicago Medical Center, after Titus had died.

"We told Cyrus, 'Your brother Titus is dead. He didn't make it. He is in heaven.' Cyrus just said to us, 'Can I go play now?' He didn't understand fully that night, but the next day he cried.

"The next morning we wanted to go pick up flowers for the wake and I was getting Cyrus dressed and I still had a big tummy. Cyrus accidentally hit my stomach and said, 'I'm sorry Titus.' I looked at Cyrus and said, 'Don't you remember Cyrus, yesterday Titus died. He's not in my stomach anymore.'

"Cecil was in the kitchen at the time and I remember I looked to him for help," Angie said.

"Cyrus then asked me, 'But why?'" Angie said, "and I told him again, 'Remember, he didn't have kidneys.' That's when Cyrus started to cry. He cried a long time."

When this book was written, Cyrus was 7. I spoke with him about his brother's death. His mom was present during the interview.

Cyrus told us that he was still upset that he didn't get to see Titus while he was in the hospital. "It hurt my feelings," Cyrus said, speaking to his mom. "Why didn't you guys let me see him?"

His mom replied, "Remember, he had a lot of tubes in him and it was kind of scary."

Angie and Cecil also chose to keep Cyrus at home with family friends during the wake and funeral. "We told him that we were taking care of stuff for Titus," Angie said. "We felt that at his age, a comprehension of a funeral and wake would not be there."

Cyrus said that he still feels sad about his brother dying.

I asked him what he does to make himself feel better when he starts to feel sad.

"I just ignore it," he replied.

Cyrus and Angie have always been close, Angie said. "He got me through things after Titus died," Angie said. "He would cry and he always talked about Titus to me, to friends and to strangers. I always let him know it was okay to talk about his brother and cry. I tried to teach him not to be angry, but to attach happiness with Titus.

"Cyrus is my first born. I'm very protective of him," Angie said. "He has endured way more than any child should have at his age. He tells things like they are. He doesn't sugarcoat things. His feelings are real and he is very softhearted. We allow him to express how he feels about Titus."

The summer after Titus died, Angie was outside with Cyrus and a butterfly started flying around them. "Cyrus said to me, 'Mom, that butterfly is so pretty. I bet it's a boy butterfly and it's Titus saying Hi!' It was amazing. That butterfly just hovered around us and wouldn't go away. Now every time we see a butterfly we say, 'That's Titus saying Hi.'"

Angie asked Cyrus, "What did we tell you you're supposed to do when you feel sad about Titus? When you feel sad you need to talk about Titus and talk to us. Or, if you want to bring something to the cemetery tell us and we'll do it."

During this interview, Cyrus told his mom that he wanted to be alone at Titus' grave the next time they went. He wanted to talk to Titus alone, not with his sisters and parents nearby.

"He's an amazing kid," Angie said. "He always tells his friends and strangers, 'These are my sisters and I have a brother who is in heaven.'"

We both asked Cyrus what would make him feel better about his brother's death. Cyrus answered quickly, "If he was here."

His mom explained to him again, "If you need to talk about Titus, talk to us. Don't be angry. Talk when you need to. Cry when you need to and never forget him. When you forget, what happens? Your heart gets sad and cold."

Around Angie's neck is a necklace. It displays a pendant with each of her children's birthstones, including one for Titus. "No one gets this necklace," Angie said. "I sleep with it, take a bath with it on. I won't take it off."

Cyrus looked at her necklace and said, "I want a necklace to wear for Titus." Angie never knew he felt this way.

Angie and Cecil have always kept photos displayed in their home of Titus, including a portrait a friend drew of him. Surprisingly, Cyrus told his mom during the interview that he didn't like to have Titus' pictures up because, as he said, "He's not here."

His mom responded, "But he *is* Cyrus. Even though he's in heaven with God, he lives in us, in our hearts. He's always here."

Every year Angie and Cecil and their children do something special on Titus' birthday to honor him. They may have a special dinner at home, or a birthday cake and wear party hats.

As a tribute to Titus on his birthday, each year Angie also places a poem and picture of him in a local newspaper.

Going through a special box of items Angie kept from Titus' birth and funeral, Cyrus held some of the items and started to cry.

"He remembers," Angie said, comforting her son. "He was only 3, but he remembers."

Cyrus Bellephant, age 3, kisses the headstone for his brother, Titus. Cyrus visits Titus' grave with his mom and sisters from time to time.

"I am always looking for a way to share about his life. To me Titus is way more special than any Nobel Prize-winning scientist. He was a strong fighter for being so small."
- Angie Bellephant

Chapter 11

"I live my life around February 3," Angie said, which is the day Titus was born and died. "I have to celebrate birth and death on the same day. Titus could be dead 15 years and I will always remember his birthday and death."

Titus is not just recognized by Angie and her family on his birthday, they have memorialized him year-round in various ways throughout their home and their lives.

"Every year for his birthday, I put his picture and a poem in the local newspaper," Angie said. "Some people criticize me for this, but I will never stop doing it."

When anyone talks to Angie about her children, she speaks of Titus openly. "I tell them I had a son who died. He didn't have kidneys and he lived 15 hours," Angie said. "I have met wonderful people, great friends by sharing information about Titus. Good things can come out of sharing."

At Titus' grave, Angie places artificial flowers and freshens them when they become weathered.

Friends of the family who live in Kentucky planted a tree in their yard in honor of Titus. These friends Angie met through the International Potter's Syndrome Support

Family. They shared with Angie and Cecil a photo of Titus' memorial tree. By the base of the tree is a plaque with Titus' name. The family has planted many memorial trees in what they call their "Angel Garden" for infants who have died.

Around her neck, Angie always wears a necklace that features a birthstone pendant for each of her children, including Titus.

A concrete statue of an angel sitting in a basket rests on the Bellephant's front porch. Angie and Cecil selected it to display at Titus' wake and funeral.

A specially decorated, large box sits safely on a shelf in Angie's closet. It contains many items from the time that she learned she was pregnant with Titus until after his death. Some of these items, greeting cards and photos, were displayed throughout the Bellephant home for a while. Angie looked through the box and shared some of the items with me. Among them are:

• Four small stuffed animals, including two teddy bears, a lamb and a duck. All were displayed at Titus' wake and funeral.

• A blue colored toy motorcycle. Blue is Angie's favorite color and her father, Franklin, loves to ride motorcycles.

• A copy of the poem "*I asked God*" that was handed out to visitors at Titus' wake and funeral.

• A taped recording of Titus' funeral service.

• A list of "commandments" titled *"After I've lost my baby, please...,"* taken from The Compassionate Friends/St. Louis, Mo., September-October 1986 newsletter. (See Chapter 20.)

• Many sympathy cards sent to the Bellphants after Titus died.

• The bulletin from her church that noted Titus' death.

• The signed guest book from Titus' wake and funeral.

• A sympathy card from international evangelist, Joyce Meyer, that was sent to Angie after Titus died. "I had reached out to her for prayer while Titus was still alive," Angie said.

• A sympathy card from a nurse in the University of Chicago Medical Center neonatal intensive care unit.

• A quote from a sympathy card that reads, "*Earth has no sorrow that heaven cannot heal.*"

• A photo of Titus after he was born. In this image, Titus had his eyes half-open. It's the only image the Bellephants have of their son's eyes.

• The original copy of a poem Cecil wrote for Titus after he died. The poem is titled "*My Son (an added essence)*" (*See Chapter 20.*)

• Images from the level 2 ultrasound when the Bellephants learned Titus had no kidneys. The date on the images reads, "*November 11, 9:17 a.m.*"

• Items from an International Potter's Syndrome Support Family gathering that was held in Frankenmuth, Michigan shortly after Titus died.

• Photos and information from a Mothers of Preschoolers program held in Angie's hometown. During a MOPS meeting after Titus died, a balloon launch was held in his honor.

• Nametags that Angie has worn at conferences where she has spoken since Titus died.

• Newspaper clippings about Titus from before he was born and throughout the years since his death.

• The pregnancy test from the day Angie learned she was pregnant with Titus. "I saved the positive pregnancy tests I took for all of my children," Angie said.

• Memorable items from Titus' stay at the University of Chicago Medical Center, including "everything that had his name on it," Angie said. She has his footprints, the nametag from his bed, a lock of his hair, a stocking cap from the hospital that Titus wore and a small blanket that "still smells like baby powder," identification bands that were around her wrist and Titus' wrist after he was born, a sign from the outside of her birthing room door that read "*It's a boy!*" and Titus' birth and death certificates.

• Every bill that the Bellephants received after his hospitalization. "Those bills were hard to look at after he had died," Angie said. "They all had his name on them and they kept coming and coming."

• A letter written by a lady who read about Titus' diagnosis of Potter's Syndrome in a local newspaper. "She said that the day we buried Titus, she received a message from Titus in heaven," Angie said. "She said Titus came to her and said, '*Today I sat on Jesus' lap and he told me how much he loves me*,' and that '*There is no pain or hospitals in heaven, just beautiful streets of gold.*' She also wrote that Titus told her, '*When our family gets here we will run and play together in heaven and make up for the time we didn't have together.*'"

"I am always looking for a way to share about his life," Angie said. "To me Titus is way more special than any Nobel Prize-winning scientist. He was a strong fighter for being so small. There are days when I am weak and want to cash it all in, and then I think about him. Titus didn't do that. He fought to live. Cecil always associates Titus with good and happy thoughts."

Angie said that pictures of Titus on their wall at home, along with photos of their other children, sometimes spark negative comments from visitors.

"One person came to our home and told us to take Titus' pictures down and put them in a box," Angie said. "I would never do that. He isn't physically here for us to see, but putting him a box isn't a way to validate his life. If people come to my home and do not like his pictures on the wall, I do not give a damn. I do not worship my son like he was a God, but he was my child. He *still is* our child, and he is beautiful to us. How can you put that in a box? You can't."

Places online where you can see tributes to Titus

http://potterssyndrome.org/newsletter/winter2004.html
Under "Birthday reminders."
Titus Franklin Bellephant, February 3, 2003.

http://www.geocities.com/bellephant_family/titus.html
Photos, poems and a brief story.

http://www.potterssyndrome.org/memorials/ad-memorials.html
International Potter's Syndrome Support Family memorials.
Titus Franklin Bellephant
Born and went to heaven on February 3, 2003
(lived 15 hours)

We will always remember our angel. Titus was a fighter and was so strong for his daddy and mommy. He lived 15 hours, but 2 hours without anything on him. We got to bathe him and let him know how much he was loved and wanted. He will never be forgotten. His brother Cyrus is 3 years old and wanted his brother so much and he misses him so much, we see it. Titus, thank you for your strength and love you gave us and showed, and all the love you opened us up to. We love so much and miss you. Please watch over us, and see you real soon. Love daddy and mommy, your brother Cyrus and all the people that wanted you here with us, and that prayed for you, and that loved you.

"I felt like I was touching people and that
if I could do more, God would guide me to do it"
- Angie Bellephant

Chapter 12

After Titus died, Angie felt the need to help other moms
who had experienced the loss of a baby.

"The first thing I did on my own, within a week after
Titus died, was reach out to people I saw in the local
newspaper obituaries who lost a baby," Angie said. "I
looked at the obits every day and sent them sympathy
cards.

"I felt like I was touching people and that if I could do
more, God would guide me to do it."

Through the International Potter's Syndrome Support
Family, Angie read that some mothers who lost a child to
Potter's started support groups in their hometowns. Angie
took action by contacting a local hospital.

"A couple months after Titus died I contacted a local
hospital and started a Pregnancy and Infant Loss Support
Group that was offered every month," Angie said. That
support group did not continue very long, Angie said,
because of various reasons, including lack of members.

Angie proposed to that same hospital to create an infant
loss memorial garden at their facility. That has not come
to fruition, yet.

Three years after Titus' death, Angie met a nurse from a
local hospital. She told Angie that she was a student in a
course on *Dying, Loss and Grief* that was taught by Karen

Kavanaugh, RN, PhD, FAAN, Professor at the University of Illinois at Chicago. The nurse referred Angie to Dr. Kavanaugh.

Angie was asked by Dr. Kavanaugh to speak to nursing students about Titus' condition, her decision not to abort him, and ultimately losing her son. After publicly telling her son's story, Angie realized that she has a gift for public speaking. "I realized that I was inspiring people," Angie said.

Dr. Kavanaugh invited Angie back to the UIC several more times where she presented her story in a session titled, *Caring for Families Who Experience a Pregnancy Loss or Newborn Death*. For this session, she spoke to undergraduate nursing students who are in a bachelor of science degree in nursing program.

Each time Angie has spoken at these events, students have asked her when she will write a book about losing her son. That's why she created this written tribute to Titus. It is a book parents can hold quietly and read slowly. It is a book to help family members, nurses and doctors see that the decision to continue carrying a baby is ultimately up to the parents.

In the future, Angie would like to create a national Potter's Syndrome Awareness Month, she said. Another idea is to set up a memorial fund in Titus' honor so funds can be channeled to families that cannot pay for their baby's funeral or headstone.

"If there is one thing I have learned from Titus is that it doesn't matter how tired I am or if I feel I have nothing left to give, I will be there for a mom in need. I will listen to her," Angie said. "I remember going with a mom to her six-week doctor checkup after she lost her baby. Even if it means I need to cook dinner for a mom and her family, I will do it."

*"I know there is a hole in my heart,
but Titus holds that missing piece.
He didn't steal it; he is borrowing it ...
this thought brings me peace."*
- Angie Bellephant

Chapter 13

The day of Titus' wake Angie said she started producing milk.

"I remember getting out of the shower and telling Cecil, 'It's one thing that Titus died, but now look at me.' It was really bad. I produced a lot of milk with Titus, so much that my breasts were in pain. I was at the wake that evening and my breasts were leaking milk. I knew people would be hugging me at the wake. Some people suggested that I wear a smaller bra because it would help. I remembered my grandmother used to say that women wrapped themselves with elastic bandages to stop the milk flow. So that night, I wrapped my chest with two elastic bandages. That night I sat most of the evening and greeted people. My milk didn't go away until the following Tuesday (four days later)."

Then Angie faced the feeling of achy arms, a painful symptom felt by many moms who have lost an infant.

"My doctor thought I was crazy when I said my arms ached," Angie said. "Everyone seemed to think I was crazy for feeling aching arms. At first I thought I was having a heart attack. It was hurting all through my arms, tingling. If I hugged a pillow tightly, it would ease up a little. This lasted three weeks. Holding Cyrus didn't help me either. I couldn't squeeze him tight enough to stop the pain. Cecil tried to massage my arms, but there were times I didn't want him to touch me. Sometimes I would take my fists and pound on my arms to stop the pain."

Grieving is an emotional response to death. Mourning is the way a person deals with those emotions. Angie recalled how her emotions soared and fell.

"There were times that I felt like Cecil had killed my son because he carries the BOR gene," Angie said. BOR is the acronym for a dominant genetic condition called Branchio-oto-renal. BOR is one of the known genetic disorders that can cause Bilateral Renal Agenesis (the absence of kidneys like Titus had). (*See Chapter 17 for BOR information.*)

"For that reason, I didn't want him to touch me when he tried to comfort me," Angie said. "I know it wasn't his fault, but I honestly hated him. I was so disgusted. I thought, 'Why us? Why not someone else in his family?' It took me a long time before I could tell him that I was angry about this.

"Then I started to feel angry with Titus because he left me," Angie said. "I asked Titus many times, 'Why did you leave me?'"

When you lose a child, Angie said, you try to be the same person, but you are never the same again.

"People kept telling me nice things like, 'God needed another angel,' or 'He's in a better place.' You grow tired of hearing the clichés. What would have made me feel better was if people just said to me, 'I don't have anything I can say except that I'm sorry.' That would have been the best thing they possibly could have said.

"Some people asked me, 'What can I do?' I would tell them, 'Can you bring Titus back? No. So then there is nothing you can do.'"

Support from family and friends usually comes the first week or two after losing an infant, Angie said. "People call and bring you meals and such, but then you are thrown back into reality, doing dishes and laundry," Angie said.

"When Titus died, Cecil had a week off of work to help plan the wake and funeral. Then he had the following week off. We should have gone on vacation. Instead, we used our money to pay off Titus' headstone. We should have gotten away because I was so vulnerable and exposed. It is like you cut yourself and it scabs over, but then the scab comes off and the wound is still there. We tried to get back to normal after that, but you are not normal after losing a child. You are so different.

"The nights were the hardest for me. It was then, in the quiet, that I missed Titus the most," Angie said. "There were nights when I felt someone had stolen him from me, that he was just missing and I couldn't get him back.

"After Titus was buried, there were times that I wanted to go out to the cemetery and dig him up," Angie said. "I didn't want him out there alone in the cold ground.

"I thought about taking sleeping pills because I couldn't sleep. I still have trouble sleeping today, four years later. I had night terrors, panic attacks. I would dream that Titus was crying and I couldn't find him to comfort him. In the dreams I would go to the crib, his swing and bassinette and he wasn't there. I would freak out and think someone stole him. I had that dream every night."

Six weeks after Titus was born, Angie had to visit her obstetrician/gynecologist for a routine exam. Unfortunately, she went alone.

"I didn't want to go," Angie said. "I was sitting there with all these women who had their new babies and they were so happy, and they had every right to be. But, I felt robbed of my baby.

"I remember the nurse during that exam, she said to me, 'How is your baby?' Moms usually bring their babies with them for their first exam. That nurse didn't know Titus died. I broke down crying.

"When I walked out of the doctor's office I thought to myself that I could never go back there," Angie said. "I was strong, I thought, until that day. I remember sitting in my car in the parking lot and I said to God, 'I hate you so much. I can't stand you.' This was too much for three people to handle, and there I was handling it the best I could, by myself. I was done. I was thrown into a fire and completely burnt up. There was nothing left for me to give to anyone.

"I thought about killing myself," Angie confessed. "But then reality hit me. I thought, 'If I kill myself, my son Cyrus will have lost a brother and a mom, and he'd be angry at God and angry with Titus, because in a sense, Titus caused his mom to kill herself.'"

Even though she was angry with Cecil, Angie said he was the one who helped her through her mourning. "He was and still is my solid rock. I can count on Cecil when no one else is there."

Angie said she still hasn't found peace with God. "Part of me died the day Titus died," she said. "A little part of me died the day we received the news that Titus had Potter's Syndrome, then carrying him each day something more was chipped away at me, and then he died. It's like there is a hole in me now and nothing can refill it.

"There is only one Titus," she said. "And, I'm not the same Angie."

Now four years after Titus' death, Angie said she is reading the Bible and attending church again. "I do believe God is a good God. He hears your prayers and cries. I also believe I will see Titus again some day, but at the same time, I think to myself, 'What did Titus do to God?' Nothing. He was innocent. I have struggled with my faith since Titus left us."

Today Angie looks back at the day Titus was born, when he was holding her fingers in the NICU at the University of Chicago Medical Center. "I envision Titus smiling at me," Angie said. "He never smiled. But I see him smiling like he was trying to say, 'It's okay mom.' In a way, I think he said that to me when he held my finger."

Titus holds Angie's fingers in the University of Chicago Medical Center NICU. He never opened his eyes for his mom, but Cecil saw his eyes for a moment before Angie arrived at the UofC. 'There was strength there in Titus' eyes,' Cecil said.

Angie did seek professional counseling after Titus died. "When I told my counselor that I was angry at God, my counselor didn't understand," Angie said. "I also wanted to have another baby, but my counselor advised me that I shouldn't. That was just a couple months after Titus died.

"I wanted another child, but I was scared to try," Angie said. "It was Dr. (Naina) Batish (her pediatrician) who gave me courage and hope to have more children. I asked her 'Would you try again?' Dr. Batish told me, 'Yes.' So I said, 'Okay.' People in our lives told us we were nuts to try again, that we shouldn't risk it. But you can't live in fear.

"I would do the same things over again that we did for Titus," Angie said. "Even as painful as it was for all of us, we have learned how to manage."

Angie went on to have two healthy daughters, but she still would like to have another boy. "Another baby boy would be good for our family," Angie said. "I hope that God grants this for us.

"Sometimes I feel like my life is incomplete without Titus. I know that's sad, but I really feel like there is a hole in my life," she said. "Sometimes I don't feel like I'm good enough for my family because Titus passed away. I know Titus cannot be replaced, but a feeling of completeness would come for me if I had another baby boy. I could also give Cyrus a brother. That means a lot to me. He really wants a brother.

"Every time we look at our family pictures, there is someone missing, and that will always be the case," Angie said. "When I die some day, my obituary will read, 'Proceeded in death by infant son, Titus.'

Angie would also like to give her husband the gift of another son.

"I remember one day that Cecil was out with Cyrus for a father and son day," Angie said. "I remember thinking to myself, 'They are out there enjoying the day and Titus would have been with them.' It had to really hurt Cecil. When Cecil came home that day I told him that I was angry that Titus could not be with them. Cecil told me he thought about Titus during their outing. Later that night Cecil told me he felt sadness and grief over Titus. It is times like that, when Cecil shares his feelings, that I will always treasure. I told Cecil that I need to know that he loved Titus and cared and would have done anything for him as much as I would have.

"There are times that I feel that Titus is just on vacation or he is sleeping," Angie said. "To me it's a coping mechanism."

Three years after Titus died, Angie visited another counselor. This counselor suggested that she start taking antidepressant medication to stop feeling the way she did. Angie didn't go back to that counselor.

"I am my own counselor now. I know what I need to do, and what I can handle," she said.

"I had told this counselor that I wanted to write a book about Titus, and my counselor advised me not to. My counselor told me that it would just rehash bad memories and it would not be good for me. I knew, however, that it would be helpful.

"I also tried to talk to my pastor, but most pastors are men and many do not know how to relate to a mom who has lost a baby."

Every day Angie still wonders about things that "could have been" with her son.

"You wonder about things like the Easter Bunny and how Titus would have reacted," she said. "You just go through emotions. They overtake you.

"My girls know that Titus is in heaven. We have told them this. With every new child we have, we have to retell the story of losing Titus over and over again to little ears, eyes and hearts.

"Titus' story will never be over for us," Angie said.

When Titus died, he took part of Angie with him, she said.

"People tell me that I'm not the same Angie they once knew. A piece of my heart was ripped out the day Titus died. I will never get that back. Titus took that piece. He came to us to give to us, and as a gift to him I gave him a piece of my heart to take with him to heaven. He is entitled to have that piece of me, and a piece of his father's heart. I have focused on this idea lately. I know there is a hole in my heart, but Titus holds that missing piece. He didn't steal it; he is borrowing it. You see, I like to control things in my life, but this thought of Titus just borrowing a piece of my heart for now, this thought brings me peace."

"I wouldn't say anything. I would simply listen,
because no words I could say would comfort them."
- Angie Bellephant

Chapter 14

"Stand up for what you believe in. Stand up for your parental rights. Nobody has a right to force you into something you don't want to do. This is your child. Do not take 'No' for an answer. That's what I learned with Titus. You cannot take 'No' for an answer."

Angie can't stress this enough to parents who have been told their unborn child has Potter's Syndrome and they do not want to terminate the pregnancy.

She is thankful for her pediatrician, Dr. Batish, who would "listen" to Angie when no one else would. It is important, Angie and Cecil stressed, to find physicians who will listen to you and work with you through the pregnancy, birth and after.

"Dr. Batish didn't sugarcoat things," Angie said. "She kept things honest with me. She promised me she would be there when Titus was born, and she was. I trusted her with the most precious gift God gave me, that is my son. She fought for Titus. She gave us time with him. She also came to Titus' wake and funeral. She is an amazing lady."

When Angie went into labor, she and Cecil were not as prepared as they could have been, Angie said. Looking back she recalls things she would have done differently.

"I wish I would have had an outfit with me for Titus to wear when he was born, not just the one provided by the

NICU," Angie said. "Even though they said we could deliver Titus early, we weren't prepared. He was born February 3, but he was due March 17. We didn't even have a camera with us."

Angie said to make sure you have a bag packed well ahead of time, even a few months before. Include in that bag a camera with batteries (charged), and a lot of film.

"We would have video taped the birth too and our time with Titus after, even if authorities in the hospital told us we couldn't," she said.

Everything happened for the Bellephants quickly once Angie went into labor. The flurry of activity proceeded through the wake and funeral.

"So many people kept telling us what to do," Angie said. "You find that you are so tired, emotionally tired."

After Titus was laid to rest, Angie and Cecil carried on with their lives; they raised their son Cyrus and Cecil had to return to work. Angie said she now regrets not taking a break as a family.

"We should have taken a vacation away from here, away from family and friends," she said. "There were just days when I didn't want to talk about Titus, but you are forced to keep going back into reality."

When asked what she would say to a mother and father of a child just diagnosed with Potter's, Angie paused, tears formed in her eyes and she said, "I'd say I'm sorry. There are no words to describe how you will feel. It sucks because your mind will race every moment to think of how you can possibly save your child.

"You can't tell another Potter's mom or dad that their decision is wrong," Angie said. "From one Potter's parent to another, we all deal differently. We chose to carry our son; others may choose to abort. The bottom line is, you do not want your child to suffer, so if you are told that your child is suffering, you will do what you can to end that suffering. If that means having an abortion, then parents may choose that route. You always keep in mind if your baby is suffering or not.

"If you have a hard time visiting your doctor so much during your pregnancy, don't go as often," Angie said. "It's your choice, your body, your baby. If you want an ultrasound every week, then ask for one. If they tell you that you don't need steroid shots, but you want them, take a stand and say you want them. We all must remember, even medical staff, that you do not have a right to tell other people how to live their lives.

"Titus wasn't perfect by medical team standards, but he was perfect to us," Angie said. "You see, Titus was made in love, so why would I not love him for the rest of his life? He was whole and complete to us. And, God loved us enough to give us Titus.

"I strongly believe in the vision I had while carrying Titus, that Titus asked God to let him stay with us for a little while," Angie said. "Titus asked for time to be with his mom and dad. And he got that."

When asked what Angie would say to someone who just lost a child to Potter's, she replied, "I wouldn't say anything. I would simply listen, because no words I could say would comfort them. The best thing for a parent to do is to talk and feel free to talk, and not get shut down and told by anyone that they aren't doing something in their grieving process the *right* way. There is no *right* way to grieve.

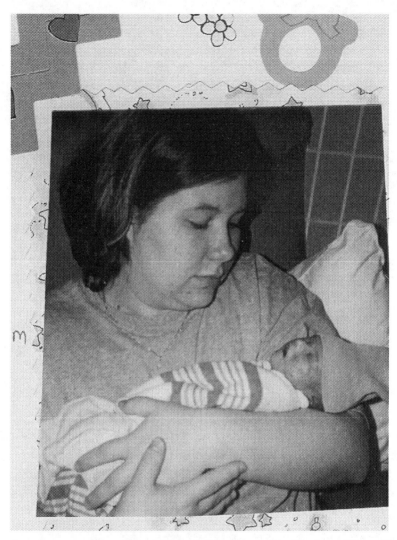

Angie spends time with Titus in the University of Chicago Medical Center NICU. At this point he had been removed from life support.

"It's a rough road and I would never want someone to go down this road. Sometimes people have the best intentions when they say something to a parent who has lost a child, they mean well, and you know they love you and care for you ... but...

"Remember that people really do want to help you," Angie said. She recalled times when friends and family offered to help her after Titus died. At that time, Angie only wanted one thing. "I remember telling people, 'Can you bring Titus back? Then no, you cannot help me.'

"I remember those first couple of weeks after he died. That's not really when you need help. You need help later on, when you are forced back into the reality of living," Angie said. "When you don't want to go out of the house to buy groceries, that's when you need help.

"I tell women who face losing a baby, 'Don't allow yourself to be put into a situation where you are around another pregnant mom or new mother. Get out of there. Go to the nearest exit.'

"I asked people in my life to talk to Cecil first and he judged whether he thought I could handle their news or questions," Angie said. "For example, one time a friend of mine wanted to tell us she was pregnant. Cecil decided if he should tell me this or not.

"When I do motivational speaking today, I have been asked by nursing students, 'Would you have gotten pregnant knowing your baby could die or have Potter's Syndrome?'" Angie said.

"I tell them, 'Yes. It is worth it. As goofy as that may sound and as hard as it is physically and emotionally to bury a child, it was worth it.'

"There are many really great things that came out of carrying Titus and losing him," Angie said. "Some people we met during that time are still close to us today. Some people have asked me why I wanted to write this book. I tell them that it's not for me. I'm doing it for other parents. I have to turn my mourning into glory."

"...something in (his) look will forever give me strength to go on day to day. I remember those eyes.
It wasn't a smile, or a frown. God says that strength is made perfect in our weaknesses. There was strength there in Titus' eyes."
- Cecil Bellephant

Chapter 15

When Titus was diagnosed with Potter's Syndrome, what was your reaction to the physician's words?

"The doctor who told us was very cold," said Cecil, recalling Monday, Nov. 11, 2002 when Angie had a level II ultrasound examination at the University of Chicago Medical Center. "He was straightforward. It was like tossing daggers at us with words. He wasn't harsh, but he was cold.

"He told us, 'Your baby has Potter's Syndrome; he's not going to live. You have two choices, you can either abort him, or keep him and he will die when he is born, if he makes it that long. What is it going to be?'"

Cecil said he had prayed all weekend, believing their son would be all right.

"We had no idea what we were going to be faced with when we went to the UofC," Cecil said. "The doctor's words were worse than seeing that Angie didn't have any fluid in the womb. That was the worst thing in the pregnancy – hearing that doctor's words - getting slapped in the face like that. Anyone would have broke down or started throwing punches."

Cecil thanks God that he had "enough sense" to pray before that day.

"The doctor was looking straight at us like he had just told us 'You're going to have to cut all your hair off' or something simple like that. He talked like the decision meant nothing," Cecil said, noting that he looked the physician in the eyes. "Right away faith just came forward. I said 'No. I refuse to accept that.'"

"He looked at me like I had just insulted him," Cecil said. "He then told us 'You mean you are going to *keep* this baby?'

"I said, 'You are darn right! That's our baby,'" Cecil said with passion in his voice. "It's wrong how our society looks at things as though babies are just tampons – you just take them and throw them in the garbage - like you just throw them away and don't think about them again. That's sickening to me.

"I want to tell any man and woman dealing with this diagnosis of Potter's Syndrome, your baby is not a throw-away. Babies have hearts, limbs. They may not be as big as we are, but they are alive. Give them a chance. You never know what can happen. Even as hard as it was for us to go through this, it was the longest four months ever after finding out Titus had Potter's Syndrome, but we are changed by the 15 hours we got to spend with him.

"We will never be the same," Cecil said. "We are broken, but we are better and beautiful before God."

You and Angie had discussed that when Titus was born, you were not going to place him on extended life support. But after he was born, and Angie was recovering, your pediatrician placed Titus on life

support. Describe what you were feeling at that time?

"We didn't give up on him," Cecil said.

"I know Angie and I agreed to not put him on life support, but if we wouldn't have put him on life support we would have never experienced his character," Cecil said. "I guess the decision was just like when we chose to not abort Titus.

"Titus was born black in color," Cecil said with tears in his eyes. "If we hadn't put him on life support, we would have never been able to see him turn pink and we would have never been able to pray over him.

"And I would never have seen his eyes," Cecil said, pausing. "I saw his eyes. Twice. Angie never got to see his eyes."

In those eyes, Cecil said he saw strength.

"It was something," Cecil said, pausing with tears in his eyes. "It was a look - something in that look that will forever give me strength to go on day to day. I remember those eyes. It wasn't a smile, or a frown. God says that strength is made perfect in our weaknesses. There was strength there in Titus' eyes."

When Titus was in the NICU at the University of Chicago Medical Center, physicians told you and Angie that Titus had no kidneys and the most humane thing you could do was take him off of life support and let him go. You initially refused to do that. You insisted on praying longer, praying that God would grant him kidneys. When Angie and the medical team left the NICU, you were alone with Titus. You said that's when God spoke to you and

changed your heart. You decided to let him go. What made you change your mind?

"The doctor had told us once that Titus had no kidneys," Cecil said during a eulogy at Titus' funeral service. "He had lungs, but he had no kidneys. A kidney specialist even came and said there was nothing they could do. The doctor told us the most humane thing that we could do was to take him off of the ventilator and let him pass peacefully.

"I didn't take that too lightly," Cecil said. "I started praying – 'We are going to get some kidneys in here!'

"For some reason, at that time, the nurses left, the doctors left and Angie left the room. That was God's way of isolating me with Titus.

"As I was sitting beside him praying, a peace came over me. A peace. And the Spirit spoke to me and said the scripture, *'Love is not self-seeking.'* (1 Cor 13:4-8)"

"Angie and I keeping Titus on a ventilator would have been for our own selfish reasons, to keep him here with us for a longer period of time. But in that one moment when everyone left the room, I was confronted with a question to myself, 'Do I *truly* believe and understand that there is a heaven where we will have a regenerated body, where Titus will not suffer and there is no grief or anger or hate? Do I truly believe this?

"I thank God He gave Titus to us in that short amount of time so we could give him back to God," Cecil said. "I thank God for this."

You wrote a poem in honor of your son called "My Son (an added essence)." *(See Chapter 20 for this* *poem.)* **When was it written and what was the inspiration behind it?**

Cecil kisses his son Titus on the cheek while seated in the University of Chicago Medical Center NICU. Titus had already been removed from life support.

85

"Shortly after Titus passed away, maybe two months after, I was at home with Angie and we were talking," Cecil said. "It was after the shock of losing our son had lifted and the real feelings, the reality had set in that we had a baby that died and was buried. We were trying to deal with feelings that couldn't be expressed. You try to find ways to express those feelings.

"The poem and friends who had ears to listen were ways we expressed ourselves," Cecil said.

"The poem was a reflection of how I believe God looks at things," he said. "There is a (Christian) song I found hope in by Bethany Dillon (called '*Hallelujah*'). In that song she says 'only you can see the good in broken things.' We had to try to see something beautiful out of something that was so ugly at the time. And her song talks about using that pain to build on.

"God gave me a voice through the poem that I wrote for Titus," Cecil said. "Before Titus was born and died, we thought that we had been through something, we had been through a lot in life; but all that stuff is like cookies and milk compared to what we went through with Titus."

Angie was angry for a time in her grieving process. She was mad about the genetic condition you carry (BOR or Branchio-oto-renal), which can lead to Potter's Syndrome. Tell me how you reacted when she confessed this anger to you.

"I was apologetic. I felt confused. Hurt," Cecil said. "Dealing with Potter's Syndrome and having to bury a child had never happened to us.

"Some things that a mom might say to anyone during that time is usually not them speaking ... they just don't know how to deal with life at the time," Cecil said. "You are, in essence, dealing with death. Some of the things Angie said in those times … some of the things I said … there is so much frustration and anger and all things bottled in one. You have to forgive.

"Dealing with a Potter's baby is an unbelievable thing," Cecil said. "There is no way you can deal with it. You can't get a handle on it. Anyone who really cares for and wants his or her child, and wants to hold that child, you have to face the fact that your child is being stripped away from you. There is absolutely nothing you can do. Those emotions are unbearable. I don't care who you are. There is no one on this planet who can bear it, swallow it and walk that out in a perfect manner."

In your healing/grieving process, have you reached a point of acceptance yet?

"Grieving is a continuous process," Cecil said. "You have to focus on finding happiness. We have to find happiness and live our lives to the fullest for Titus."

At Titus' funeral Cecil spoke about the biblical story of Shadrach, Meshack and Abednego in the fiery furnace. King Nebuchadnezzar made an image of gold and set it up in Babylon. He ordered that whenever the people heard the sound of music they should bow down and worship the image or else be thrown into a blazing furnace. But Shadrach, Meshack and Abednego would not bow down or worship the image. They obeyed God and had faith God would protect them if they were thrown into the flames. Cecil stressed that we should also not "bow down before the golden image" which is man's opinions and temptations. We should have faith in God.

"That image is always before us and we have to have the courage every day to say 'I'm not going to bow. I'm not giving up. I'm not giving in. I'm going to keep the forward march and today is going to be a good day,'" Cecil said.

"Every morning when I wake I say 'Today is going to be a good day. Great things are going to happen for me and my family,'" Cecil said. "You have to wake up with that on your mind. I know that we will always have the temptation to give in, to give up, to bow before that golden image, but we have to make a conscious decision to say 'No, I'm not.'

"We have had two babies since we lost Titus, and that temptation to bow is still there all then time. But you know, great and mighty things have happened for us since then. It is only the tip of the iceberg of what is going to happen for us."

How did you support your wife when she was carrying Titus and after his death? Was there anything you would have done differently in giving her that support?

"The biggest thing that a man can do is to listen to their wife (or partner)," Cecil said. "You need to have your ears open and hold your partner. Listen and don't judge them. Let them grieve. There is no wrong or right way to grieve."

Cecil realizes that he channeled most of his energy into reading the Bible during the time Angie was carrying Titus. Now he regrets it.

"It was good to read the Bible, but I dug my head into it and overdid it," Cecil said. "Women accept things and men have to fix things. I did the best I knew how to do at the time – asking God to fix it because He is a healing God. But while God gives, He also takes away.

"I tried to go to God and fix things. But while I was soaking all that scripture in, I neglected Angie and Cyrus in a way," Cecil said. "Because, think about it ... if God is truly going to fix something, then I do not have to petition him 24 hours a day to fix it. I could talk to God and still love my family.

"In a lot of ways I caused more hurt than I did healing at that time," Cecil said, "because I was so bent on Titus being healed that I forgot to love throughout that time. Faith is good, but faith is not the greatest thing, love is. Sometimes people have faith, but they forget to love.

"If this confession will help to open another man's eyes who is trying to 'fix' the situation for his child and wife, just remember that it is good to have faith but we have to remember that God is God. Sometimes you have to leave some things with Him and do the best you can while you are here on earth."

Watching your wife through carrying Titus and now in her healing process after his birth/death, how would you describe her character?

"Any woman who can weather losing a child, being in pain physically and carrying a condemned child around in their womb and come out in their right mind is a trooper ... you know ... to go through Potter's Syndrome and come out on the other side without your child and have to go on living life and look back and remember that ..." Cecil paused. "If after all that you aren't strung out on drugs, if you're not getting drunk every night trying to numb the pain, if you are still functioning and you are still able to take care of your family, cook dinner, clean the house ... there is something special about that woman. There is no word to describe it. I admire this in my wife, very much, and in other women I see who have lost children.

"We have a friend who has lost two children back-to-back and she is still functioning – still pressing on through life," Cecil said. "Angie is still pressing on, every day. No, everything isn't perfect – every day has struggles and temptations where you want to throw in the towel. You remember (carrying a Potter's child and burying him) every day. You wake up and things come back to you. You have to say 'No.'

"I love Titus and I prayed for him every day. I didn't give up on him, but he wasn't in my stomach," Cecil said. "I didn't go through the physical pain Angie did. I didn't go through as much mental anguish as Angie did. I got to go to work and get away from the situation. I got to go and maybe laugh every once in a while. I got to read a book and be away for a little bit. But Angie had Titus in her stomach, and she was never able to get away from it. She felt his bones move inside of her because there was no fluid in the womb. I got to get away and experience other things. She did not; she always had Titus there.

"To go through something like that is torture, slow grueling torture," Cecil said. "No words can explain it. And to come out of that is a miracle of God. There are a lot of women who didn't make it out with their sanity. But Angie presses on every day. And she keeps a forward march knowing that there is a great destiny and plan for our lives that we have to fulfill, and we will fulfill it. There is no word to describe it. It is a miracle."

What advice would you give to other men on how to support their partner through the grieving process?

"After four years now, I have thought about what I could have done differently," Cecil said. "It's like in the Bible where King David was trying to bring the Ark of God to Jerusalem from the enemy's camp. There was a direct order to not touch the Ark. There was a good man named Uzzah – and the Ark was falling over and Uzzah reached up to catch the Ark and push it back up; but, he touched it. God made it very clear in the scriptures that nobody was to touch the Ark except the priests and then only when they moved it. Uzzah was killed for trying to help. Uzzah was a good man, he had good intentions, he was trying to fix things that only God can fix. That's why God said, don't touch it, because it was His work, not man's work.

"Having a Potter's baby in your wife's womb is not a manageable thing," Cecil said. "My advice is like with Uzzah, don't try to manage the unmanageable. Live your lives. If your wife asks for something, go get it for her. Don't think about finances. If you don't have money, go find some money and do it. If she wants to go to Hawaii, take her to Hawaii. If you don't have money, go finance the money and go to Hawaii. If she wants a Whopper from Burger King, go buy her a Whopper. If she wants to swear, let her do it. As long as she isn't breaking anything and hurting herself or anyone else, let her go. Let her have a couple laughs. Let her do what her heart wants to do to get away from the situation."

When it comes to giving comfort to your wife or partner, remember that sometimes they do not want to be comforted, Cecil said.

"In the Bible it says that Rachel was crying over her children and was refusing to be comforted because they were no more (Jeremiah 31:15). She was refusing to be comforted," Cecil said. "Sometimes men are going to have to weather that fact, when they try to reach out to their wife and she refuses to be comforted because there is nothing you can do. All you can do is what they ask for when they ask. Your wife will come back to you."

The nights were hard for Cecil and Angie, and still are for Angie in many regards. She finds herself unable to sleep because thoughts of Titus race through her mind. The nights also bring a sense of loneliness.

"God says that *'Weeping may endure for a night, but joy comes in the morning.'* (Psalm30:5). Even though there is happiness in the morning, you have to get through a night to get there," Cecil said.

"There were many times when Angie told me she wanted something and I tried to convince her she didn't need it. Don't do that. Listen to your wife, get a pen and paper and write it all down. Angie told me what she wanted but I didn't listen."

For example, Angie liked to go out and eat, but the Bellephants were short on money, so Cecil tried to tell her they didn't need to go out to eat.

"It was so stupid of me," he said.

Cecil also tried to get Angie to go back to church and to go out with her friends when she didn't want to go.

"Sometimes she could deal with people and sometimes not," Cecil said. "I made her do a lot of things. I listened to other people's opinions and by doing that, I did a lot more harm than good.

"The only people who can relate to you are other families that have gone through Potter's Syndrome and even *they* will not grieve the same as you will.

"We as human beings try to categorize things and you cannot do that," Cecil said. "Having a Potter's baby is an unmanageable situation."

Cecil said that he and Angie will always look at their children and think of Titus. "It doesn't matter if we have

10 more children, there will always be one child that you miss," Cecil said. "Every time you turn around in the van and you look at the kids you always kind of see that little image of what Titus might have looked like sitting next to Cyrus or fighting with him in the van. There is always someone missing in family pictures. There is a tinge of sadness there. Every blessing from God has a tinge of sadness with it, if it doesn't have that tinge of sadness, it's not from God."

Cecil emphasized the need for Potter's families to find friends and family who will listen in their time of need.

"People will try to tell you what they think you should do, what you should eat, if you should stay at home ... even if they don't know what you are going through they will think they have a right to say something," Cecil said. "It doesn't matter if they are your best friend, pastor or mother, if you don't like to hear what they are saying, kick them out of your house. Hearing some things can cause more confusion and grief on top of what you are already facing. People want to help, but there is nothing they can really say to make you feel better.

"You will have good days and you will have bad days, and I pray that you have more good days than bad days," Cecil said. "My ultimate prayer is that none of the families that read this book will be torn apart. We made it. You can make it, too."

Section II

Information, Resources
& Inspiration

*Today the incidence of Potter's Syndrome is said to be
somewhere between 1 in 2,000 and 1 in 5,000.
The average occurrence rate is approximately
1 in 4,000 births.*
- www.potterssyndrome.org

Chapter 16

*Jason Clarke is a contributing author for this chapter.

In 1946 Dr. Edith Louise Potter, (1901 - 1993), a pediatric
pathologist at the University of Chicago Lying-In
Hospital, described a unique condition among infants.

This condition was a congenital birth defect where a
developing fetus had no kidneys or the kidneys were
malformed.

Prior to this, there had been isolated studies done on
infants with the condition, some studies dating back to
the 1600s. In fact, Bilateral Renal Agenesis (the absence
of kidneys) was first recognized in 1671 by Wolfstrigel as
a defect of fetal development.

But until Dr. Potter's study in 1946, it was presumed that
the condition was extremely rare.

Dr. Potter's investigation concentrated only on total renal
agenesis, but since then the name has been extended to
any condition where the kidneys fail to develop fully.

Today Potter's Syndrome is also known as Potter
Sequence or Oligohydramnios Sequence.

It has now been defined into five distinct sub-
classifications that are noted later in this chapter.

Potter's Syndrome Research Today

Patrick Brophy, M.D. and Jason Clarke, both formerly from the University of Michigan, now at the University of Iowa, Department of Pediatrics, are renal development researchers with an interest in Bilateral Renal Agenesis in humans. Their lab is leading a study on Mutational Analysis in Selected Disorders of the Genitourinary Tract, which means that they are scanning the human genome to find the gene(s) that cause these birth defects. The study's main focus is on Bilateral Renal Agenesis and other forms of Potter's Syndrome, to include Branchio-oto-renal (BOR) syndrome.

Clarke is the primary researcher for the Bilateral Renal Agenesis (Potter Sequence/Syndrome) and BOR portions of this study. (*See Chapter 19 for Clarke's contact information.*)

The study was started when Clarke, who was studying two different strains of mice, each with its own recessive genetic mutation that leads to lethal kidney malformation, decided to mate the two strains together to study the effects the two genes had on each other. An unexpected observation noted by Clarke was that many adolescent mice carrying both of the genetic mutations were missing one of their kidneys, and that this was inherited in an autosomal dominant manner.

Also, there were fewer adolescent mice carrying both genetic mutations than would be expected – suggesting that these mice were dying after birth. When he looked at the mice in utero he found that many of the mice carrying both genetic mutations were either missing both of their kidneys, or missing one kidney with the other being severely malformed. (This study has been published; Clarke et al., *Human Molecular Genetics*, 2006: 15(**23**): 3420-3428.) These observations led Clarke to begin researching renal agenesis in humans.

Clarke found that many of the observations he saw in his mice fit with reports of Bilateral Renal Agenesis in humans. A search for others studying this birth defect in humans, to share his results with, yielded no outcome. Clarke then applied to his institution to conduct human genetic research in hopes of finding the gene(s) that are causing this birth defect in humans. He works closely with the National Potter's Syndrome Support Group and has authored research articles regarding Bilateral Renal Agenesis, BOR syndrome and informational articles about Potter's Syndrome.

Kidneys and fetal development

First, it is important to understand the function of the kidneys in a developing fetus.

All the body processes produce waste materials, which if allowed to accumulate could poison the body. Excretion is the process of cleaning this waste from the body, the skin excretes water and salt, the lungs excrete carbon dioxide and water vapor, and the kidneys excrete urine.

The kidneys are composed of a network of tubes that are all vital to the proper function of each kidney.

With Potter's Syndrome the main problem is that the kidneys are missing or severely malformed. When this happens, other health problems arise.

The primary cause of infant death due to Potter's Syndrome is not being able to breathe. By approximately the second trimester the fetal kidneys are responsible for the production of much of the amniotic fluid in the womb. In the womb, the baby inhales the fluid into its lungs causing the lungs to grow. When the kidneys are absent or not working, amniotic fluid is not produced and the lungs cannot develop properly. As a result, when the baby is born it is unable to breathe properly.

Also related to the lack of amniotic fluid are physical features of Potter's Syndrome. Without adequate amniotic fluid in the womb, an infant does not have adequate space to grow. The baby's limbs may not form properly and its face may show certain features such as a flattened nose and chin.

What did Dr. Potter's study in 1946 show?

The first study Dr. Potter did was on 20 infants who had died over a 10-year period. In the group were 17 boys and 3 girls. Of 19 available maternal histories, the mother's ages ranged from 18 to 39, giving an average age of 24. Two of these women had previous abortions. Only two had more than two previous pregnancies, one of which had 11 children. Nineteen of the mothers were white and one was black.

Dr. Potter also noted that these babies were more likely to be born alive rather than stillborn. In this group, fetal death occurred prior to labor in one infant, during labor in six infants, and after birth in 13.

The length of life for the babies varied from 25 minutes, to 11 hours and 15 minutes, giving an average life span of 1 hour and 38 minutes.

Of the 16 babies where gestation had been recorded, the number of weeks varied from 26 weeks to 40 weeks giving an average delivery time of about 32.5 weeks.

Dr. Potter was unable to establish the amount of amniotic fluid present with each baby and therefore was unable to establish the important link between the kidneys and the production of the fluid. This was only discovered and confirmed later.

The cause of the death was mainly associated to the malformation of the lungs. The children also showed similar facial features such as wide set eyes, a slightly compressed nose, low-set flat ears and a compression of the chin. Other physical features were clubbed feet and some had clubbed hands.

With the females, it was also noted that their genitalia were extremely under-developed, but with the males, their genitalia development was normal.

Dr. Potter concluded that the incidence of this condition was somewhere between 4 and 7 deaths per 1,000 deaths in newborn infants. She also noted that there was no relation to maternal age, the method of delivery or complications during pregnancy.

The infants were predominately male. The lungs of the infants were all severely underdeveloped or hypoplastic and all the infants showed characteristic facial expressions. Prior to post mortem examination, only eight of the infants were believed to have died because of malformations.

Today the incidence of Potter's Syndrome is said to be somewhere between 1 in 2,000 and 1 in 5,000. The average occurrence rate is approximately 1 in 4,000 births.

Potter's Syndrome is predominately a male condition with an occurrence rate of approximately 65 to 80 percent male babies.

Classifications of Potter's Syndrome

The most common form of Potter's Syndrome is the total absence of kidneys. There are, however, varying degrees of the condition.

There are those in the medical and research field that use the term Potter's Syndrome to refer to only cases of BRA (Bilateral Renal Agenesis - absence of kidneys), while other groups use the term to loosely refer to all instances of oligohydramnios (reduced amniotic fluid) and anhydramnios (absence of amniotic fluid) regardless of the specific cause.

Classic form

This term is traditionally used when the infant has BRA. True BRA also involves bilateral agenesis of the ureters (absence of the ducts that carry urine from the kidneys to the bladder).

Type I

Type I is due to Autosomal Recessive Polycystic Kidney Disease (ARPKD), which occurs in 1 in 16,000 infants. The kidneys of the fetus/neonate will be enlarged, have many small cysts filled with fluid and will fail to produce an adequate volume of fetal urine. The liver and pancreas of the fetus may also show fibrosis and/or a cystic change.

Type II

Type II is usually due to Renal Adysplasia that can also fall under the category known as Hereditary Urogenital Adysplasia or Hereditary Renal Adysplasia (HRA). Renal Adysplasia/HRA is characterized by the absence of one kidney and the remaining kidney being small and malformed. Bilateral Renal Agenesis is believed to be the most extreme phenotypic variation of HRA.

Type III

Type III is due to Autosomal Dominant Polycystic Kidney Disease (ADPKD) linked to mutations in the genes PKD1 and PKD2. While ADPKD is considered to be an Adult Onset Polycystic Kidney Disease, it can also appear in the fetus and neonate in rare cases. Like Autosomal Recessive Polycystic Kidney Disease, ADPKD can also appear with hepatic cysts and an enlarged spleen. An increased prevalence of vascular disease is also observed in these cases of ADPKD.

Type IV

Type IV occurs when a longstanding obstruction in either the kidney or ureter leads to cystic kidneys or hydronephrosis. Hydronephrosis is dilation of the kidney with urine, caused by backward pressure on the kidney when the flow of urine is obstructed. This can be due to chance, environment or genetics. While these types of obstructions occur frequently in fetuses, they rarely lead to fetal death.

Other

Often cystic kidneys that do not fall under the classification of being polycystic will be termed as being Multicystic Renal Dysplasia (MRD). Recently many cases of MRD have been linked to the mutations in the gene PUJO.

Another cause of Potter's Syndrome can be the rupturing of the amniotic sac that contains the amniotic fluid of the fetus. This can happen spontaneously, by chance, environment, maternal trauma and in rare cases - maternal genetics.

Is there a risk of recurrence of Potter's Syndrome?

In the vast majority of cases, Potter's Syndrome is an isolated abnormality and it is unlikely to recur in the same family. Statistically however once you have had one Potter's Syndrome baby the risk of a recurrence of some kind of kidney defect is about 3 percent. In a few cases there may be an abnormality of one kidney from either parent in which case the risk of having Potter's Syndrome again may rise to 10 percent. Even rarer still is when there is a genetic link to the syndrome, then the risk may be as high as 1 in 4.

One of the known genetic disorders that can be easily confused with BRA is a syndrome known as BOR (Branchio-oto-renal). According to recent studies, BOR is believed to occur in 1 in 40,000 people. It is estimated that 2 percent of the profoundly deaf have BOR. However, true BRA, and other forms of Potter's will lack the additional defects associated with BOR. (*Read more about BOR in Chapter 17.*)

In many cases of Potter's Syndrome, particularly BRA, it is difficult to find signs that the trait was inherited from one of the parents, and therefore the condition is deemed as a spontaneous occurrence and unlikely to happen again.

While it is known what causes the two types of Polycystic Kidney Diseases, the causes of the other forms of Potter's Syndrome are, for the most part, unknown. The research from the work of Clarke and Brophy, as well as other researchers, will hopefully prove fruitful and shed light on the subject.

When can Potter's be diagnosed?

By 12 weeks of pregnancy a baby has all its organs but due to the size of the organs the kidney's development would be difficult to assess at that stage. It is possible however to make a diagnosis from 14 weeks but it is more likely to be made from about 18 weeks.

If the diagnosis of Potter's is made this early the mother will be continually assessed during her pregnancy to see if there is any change or development.

During an ultrasound the first thing that the doctor will notice will be the extreme lack of amniotic fluid, this will suggest that there may be a kidney problem and the doctor will then do testing to establish whether or not the kidneys have developed.

If an in-depth fetal assessment is carried out on the baby, preferably at a later date in pregnancy, it will establish to a 95 percent certainty that the kidneys are absent. A further test can be done again using a scan to detect if there is any kidney function. With this test the doctor inserts a thin needle into the womb through the mother's abdomen, a procedure very similar to amniocentesis, and then can inject fluid into the baby's abdomen and track by scan to see if the fluid will travel to the baby's kidneys. On completion of this test the doctor should be about 99 percent certain of his diagnosis, leaving a 1 percent margin for error.

In some cases where the mother has not undergone an ultrasound during pregnancy, the condition may go undetected until after birth.

At birth all babies are graded on color, capacity to breathe, weight, size and general strength.

With Potter's Syndrome babies it will be visible that the child has a severe respiratory problem and may show some of the facial and physical features associated with the syndrome. If the mother has not had an ultrasound, the diagnosis might only be made by post-mortem examination.

Unfortunately because the only symptom before birth is the absence of fluid, Potter's Syndrome can be hard to diagnose before birth and will often go undetected. The fetal development usually carries on normally and at birth the babies are usually a healthy weight.

Survival chances after birth

In the womb the baby's life is dependent on the functions of the placenta. The placenta acts like a life-support system and filters products and food from the mother to the baby and then back out into the mother's system for disposal.

The amniotic fluid, which is normally a straw-colored and clear substance, consists of 99 percent water with small amounts of protein, glucose and salt and also contains shed cells from the baby. The baby's urine is mostly water because the mother's kidneys are functioning via the placenta for the baby disposing of any waste products. Therefore the baby can survive without its kidneys as long as the placenta is functioning normally. Problems for the baby usually only show after birth.

The maximum life span for a baby born without kidneys is normally only a couple of hours. Where there is some kidney development with a little kidney function, a baby's life span may be slightly longer, but the infant would probably need the aid of a respirator and kidney dialysis. The course of treatment varies case to case and physicians usually make treatment decisions.

Many parents ask if undergoing a kidney transplant can save their baby.

This would be extremely difficult. With a lack of kidneys, it is difficult to ascertain what other necessary tubes and material failed to develop.

It would also be difficult trying to keep the baby alive while waiting for a transplant. The infant may also need a lung transplant because its lungs are underdeveloped.

There would be great difficulty in getting organ donors; the donor would have to be an infant the same age and blood types would have to be matched.

In extremely rare cases where partial kidney development has been sufficient to develop the lungs to a reasonable stage, these babies can be put on respirators and then on dialysis. If they survive, in early childhood they can undergo a transplant.

Remember, the vast majority of Potter's Syndrome babies die at birth or shortly afterwards.

"In that same family, another child may carry the BOR gene and not be obviously affected by it. But for some reason, in some cases, BOR can be lethal and it will arrest renal development in utero."
- Jason Clarke, University of Iowa, Department of Pediatrics

Chapter 17

While reading information on the International Potter's Syndrome Support Family Web site, Angie Bellephant began to realize why her son Cyrus is hearing impaired. It was later confirmed at the University of Chicago Medical Center that a genetic condition runs in their family. Cecil, she learned, is the carrier.

While Angie read Web site information about Potter's Syndrome, she saw information about BOR (Branchio-oto-renal), a dominant genetic condition that can result in hearing loss, ear pits (a small depression in front of the top portion of the ear), branchial (neck) cysts or fistulas, and kidney anomalies. Three less common symptoms associated with BOR are ear tags (a mole-like growth found immediately in front of the ear), blocked tear ducts and a short palate.

One of the known genetic disorders that can cause Bilateral Renal Agenesis (the absence of kidneys like Titus had) is BOR, according to a *BOR Research Project* by Boys Town National Research Hospital in Omaha, Nebraska.

"Cecil has ear pits in front of one of his ears," Angie said about her husband. "Cecil started to lose his hearing when he was in kindergarten." It was suggested that he wear hearing aids in both ears.

"Cyrus has ear pits in front of both of his ears," she said. "Titus had an ear pit in front of one of his ears. Genesus has them in front of both of her ears."

Ear pits are found in about 80 percent of BOR cases, research shows.

Cyrus failed a newborn hearing screening and so did Genesus. Cyrus passed a follow-up hearing screening at the University of Chicago Medical Center and seemed to speak "fine," Angie said. But at the age of 6, he was diagnosed with a hearing problem. He now wears a hearing aid in one ear. Genesus "borderline passed" a follow-up hearing screening, Angie said, and now she must have her hearing tested every year.

Their daughter Joyous does not have ear pits. She passed her newborn hearing test and seems to have no problem with her hearing.

"Titus probably would have had the same hearing issues at some point in his life," Angie said.

About 90 percent of BOR patients have hearing loss, the research project said. This hearing loss can be mild or profound and can be stable or progress in severity.

When Cyrus was 2 weeks old, Angie said, he also developed a classic branchial cyst often associated with BOR. About 60 percent of BOR cases have branchial cysts, research shows.

"I noticed a jelly-like substance under Cyrus' neck and wondered what it was," Angie said. "It was hot outside at the time and I thought at first he was just sweating. The cyst on his neck had opened and saliva was coming of the hole. We had that hole surgically closed."

Angie soon learned that her husband had a branchial cyst when he was an infant, but his closed up on its own.

Genesus and Joyous did not develop the branchial cysts.

While Titus was born with no kidneys, Genesus has had mild kidney problems since she was born.

Kidney anomalies are found in about 15 percent of those with BOR, research shows. Most of the anomalies have minimal clinical significance and consist of minor changes in the anatomy of the kidney or urinary collection system. Some babies, however, face the absence of one or both kidneys.

"Genesus wasn't urinating very much," Angie said. "We had an ultrasound on her kidneys and we learned that a flap to her left kidney wasn't opening all the way to release all the urine. Because of this, she could develop infections. She may need surgery in the future to alter the flap to that kidney."

"Bilateral Renal Agenesis (BRA) can often be confused with severe cases of BOR," said Jason Clarke, University of Iowa, Department of Pediatrics. "Several factors will delineate the two birth defects, primarily of which will be a family history of BOR or others in the family that have BOR-like phenotypes/characteristics. Also, if the affected infant presents other BOR characteristics (external ear abnormalities, skin tags or pits near the ears, branchial cysts, etc.), then it is most likely a case of BOR syndrome and not true BRA."

"Classic Potter's Syndrome, or BRA, is defined as a *total* absence of the kidneys and ureters, and the absence of other abnormalities such as those associated with BOR or other syndromes," Clarke said. "In an infant that has BOR yet appears to have BRA, you will more often than not find ureters (ducts that carry urine from the kidneys to the urinary bladder), which means that some form of a kidney tissue was present at some point. You may have to use a microscope and a good pathologist to find them, but the odds are they are there.

"The ureters need to be stimulated by urine flow from the kidneys in order to develop and mature," Clarke said. "All you need to produce urine is one or two nephrons (the units in the kidney that remove waste from the blood and produce urine), you don't need a complete kidney to do this. So, if there are ureters, then there was at least some form of renal development, which is where we draw the line between BRA and other renal anomalies.

"For some reason, however, in some of these infants with severe BOR the kidneys appear to stop developing after the ureters have formed," Clarke said. "What little renal tissue may have been there just isn't enough to promote lung development or sustain the fetus after birth in some cases." Clarke has also authored a research paper on BOR Syndrome (Clarke et al., *Clinical Genetics* (2006): 70(**1**): 63-67).

According to the *BOR Research Project*, BOR is believed to occur in 1 in 40,000 people. It is estimated that 2 percent of the profoundly deaf have BOR.

While most Potter's Syndrome cases have no parental link, if a baby develops this condition it is usually considered a fluke. The same parents usually do not have more than one case in their family.

With BOR, however, the gene can carry on to other children. When a person with BOR has children, each child has a one in two chance of receiving the gene that causes BOR, according to the *BOR Research Project.*

"In that same family, another child may carry the BOR gene but not be obviously affected by it. But for some reason, in some cases, BOR can be lethal and it will arrest renal development in utero," Clarke said.

The genetics laboratory at Boys Town National Research Hospital was one of the first to determine there is a gene on chromosome 8 that causes BOR. This gene was identified by a laboratory in France. Since the gene has been identified, it can be studied. The results of the study may reveal how the mutation causes BOR and why there is such a wide variation of symptoms among people with BOR. With this understanding it may be possible to develop treatments for this condition.

Do you or your family have BOR? You can learn more about participating in this research project by contacting:

BTNRH - Genetics BOR Syndrome Project
555 North 30th Street
Omaha, Nebraska 68131
Phone: 1-800-835-1468 (voice/TTY)
E-mail: Maren Jensen, Research Assistant to William.
Kimberling, PhD Boys Town National Research Hospital
Genetics Department, jensenml@boystown.org
See: http://boystownhospital.org/Hearing/info/
genetics/syndromes/bor.asp

*"... the Web site was good for me because
I met wonderful people who I remain friends with."*
- Angie Bellephant

Chapter 18

After Angie learned that Titus had Potter's Syndrome, she channeled her efforts into finding any information she could about the condition.

Initial searches at local libraries revealed nothing, Angie said. A search online also revealed very little. But one Web site, a support group for Potter's parents called International Potter's Syndrome Support Family, became a lifeline for her.

This Web site, www.potterssyndrome.org, is a source of Potter's Syndrome information and it helps connect Potter's families. Links on this site lead to online support with other Potter's Syndrome families and access to a researcher currently working on Potter's Syndrome research.

Michele Scheben-Samuel is the owner/creator of the Web site. She created the Web site after Delores Schlegel started a Potter's Syndrome Support Group forum (through Delphi Forums LLC). Michele joined Delores in management of the support group forum and then the Web site soon followed as a need for those desiring further information and a place they could send others. You can e-mail them at: potterssyndrome@hotmail.com.

"When you first look at their site, you will be bombarded with stories by moms who lost their babies to Potter's, their personal decisions and so forth," Angie said. "Some told me that their decisions might be the best ones for me. Some aborted their child. I didn't judge them for their choices, but aborting my child wasn't an option for me. For the most part, the Web site was good for me because I met wonderful people who I remain friends with. Michele and I became friends and we are still in touch.

"Michele helped me with the emotional stages I went through," Angie said. "She would tell me to stand my ground and stick to what I believe in."

After Titus died, Angie said she communicated on the Web site every day. "If I hadn't been talking on that Web site, I think I would have had a panic attack. That Web site was my outlet."

Angie and Cecil also found hope and peace through a gathering the International Potter's Syndrome Support Family hosts yearly. The one they attended was in Frankenmuth, Michigan.

During this gathering, parents and family members who have lost a child to Potter's meet for a weekend of events. Angie was able to connect faces with names of those she had been communicating online with for months.

"I remember the memorial night where we lit candles for babies who had passed away," Angie said. Parents also spent time sharing stories about their babies.

Perhaps the most memorable part of that weekend was a balloon launch, Angie said. Helium balloons were released that carried a card with the name of a baby that died from Potter's, their parent's names and the baby's date of birth. "The launch didn't move me like it did Cecil," Angie said.

"On our drive home, Cecil pulled over to the side of the road and told me, 'I have to talk to you,'" Angie said. "He told me, 'I finally let Titus go, in peace.' Cecil had not talked about losing Titus until that day. We were finally able to talk together."

"I recommend that people go to this Web site for help," Angie said. "They also post memorials for babies who have died from Potter's."

Chapter 19

The following are sources of support and information that Angie Bellephant recommends.

The Compassionate Friends, Inc.

The mission of The Compassionate Friends is to assist families toward the positive resolution of grief following the death of a child of any age and to provide information to help others be supportive.

The Compassionate Friends is a national nonprofit, self-help support organization that offers friendship, understanding and hope to bereaved parents, grandparents and siblings. There is no religious affiliation and there are no membership dues.

The secret of TCF's success is simple: As seasoned grievers reach out to the newly bereaved, energy that has been directed inward begins to flow outward and both are helped to heal. The vision of The Compassionate Friends is that everyone who needs us will find us and everyone who finds us will be helped.

The Compassionate Friends, Inc.
P. O. Box 3696
Oak Brook, Illinois 60522-3696
Toll-free: 877-969-0010
Phone: 630-990-0010
Fax: 630-990-0246
E-mail: Nationaloffice@compassionatefriends.org
Web site: www.compassionatefriends.org

Mutational Analysis in Selected Disorders of the Genitourinary Tract

Patrick Brophy, M.D., Associate Professor of Pediatrics at the University of Iowa, Department of Pediatrics, and Jason Clarke are leading a study on Mutational Analysis in Selected Disorders of the Genitourinary Tract.

The Web site for this study, www.kidneygenes.com, is a physician resource dedicated to coordinating linkage and mutational analysis research in selected disorders of the genitourinary tract. They are enrolling eligible individuals and families to analyze genetic lesions associated with Bilateral Renal Agenesis (BRA), Bilateral Hydronephrosis and forms of Potter Sequence/Syndrome due to kidney and urinary tract abnormalities.

To date, genetic lesions associated with BRA have not been identified. However, their laboratory is currently enrolling qualified participant families for the identification and mutational analysis of genetic lesions associated with BRA (Potter Sequence/Syndrome).

Jason Clarke is the primary researcher for the BRA (Potter Sequence/Syndrome) portion of the study.

Web site: www.kidneygenes.com/potter.htm
E-mail: jason-clarke@uiowa.edu
Phone: 319-384-3040

National Potter's Syndrome Support Group

This is an information and parent match non-profit organization focusing on Potter's Syndrome.

Web site:
http://www.geocities.com/heartland/meadows/
5586/syndrome.htm

Chapter 20

My Son (an added essence)

A poem written by Cecil Bellephant
www.geocities.com/bellephant_family/angel-titus.html

My son,
when I wake up to a beautiful morning, you are there.

When I look into a multicolored sunset,
I experience that awe with you.

When Cyrus and I kneel next to his bed to pray,
I look over and on the other side of me,
I envision you there ... every time ... you are there.

I aspire to go higher heights in this life,
to see greater views, to experience bigger horizons,
to climb bigger mountains ...

and from the peak of that mountain,
as I look into the distance ...
I'll take you with me always and forever.

Lord,
with tears and joyfulness,
I give thanks today for the added essence
to my life that is ... Titus.

I asked God

Shared at Titus' wake and funeral.

I asked God to take away my habit. God said, No.
It is not for me to take away, but for you to give it up.

I asked God to make my handicapped child whole.
God said, No. His spirit is whole, his body is only
temporary

I asked God to grant me patience. God said, No.
Patience is a byproduct of tribulations; it isn't granted,
it is learned.

I asked God to give me happiness. God said, No.
I give you blessings; happiness is up to you.

I asked God to spare me pain. God said, No.
Suffering draws you apart from worldly cares and
brings you closer to me.

I asked God to make my spirit grow. God said, No.
You must grow on your own! But I will prune you to
make you fruitful.

I asked God for all things so that I might enjoy life. God
said, No. I will give you life, so that you may enjoy all
things.

I ask God to help me love others, as much as He loves
me.
God said, "Ahhh, finally you have the idea."

**To the world you might be one person, but to one
person you just might be the whole world.**

The mention of his name

Angie Bellephant's message on her
answering machine after Titus died.

The mention of his name
may bring tears to my eyes,
but it never fails to bring
music to my ears.
If you are really my friend,
let me hear the beautiful music of his name.
It soothes my broken heart
and sings to my soul.

Child's prayer

Now I lay me down to sleep;
I pray thee, Lord, my soul to keep.
If I should die before I wake,
I pray thee, Lord,
my soul to take.

Immortality

From the memorial folder at Titus' funeral

Do not stand by my grave and weep …
I am not there. I do not sleep.

I am a thousand winds that blow.
I am a diamond glint on snow.
I am the sunlight on ripened grain.
I am the gentle autumn rain.

When you awake in the morning hush,
I am the swift upflinging rush
of quiet birds in circling flight.
I am the soft stars shining at night.

Do not stand by my grave and cry …
I am not there.
I did not die.
I live with the Risen Lord!

After I've lost my baby, please ...

Taken from The Compassionate Friends/St. Louis, Mo.
September-October 1986 newsletter.
For TCF information, see
www.compassionatefriends.com

• Don't ignore me because you are uncomfortable with the subject of death – it makes me wonder if what happened to me means nothing to you.

• Acknowledge my pain, even if you think I shouldn't be feeling it because I've lost "only a baby." And please, don't expect me to be "over this" in a month (or maybe even a year or two); losing a baby is one of the most difficult of all life's experiences and the depth of my grief will even shock me as it returns in waves over and over again long after everyone else has forgotten. (Holidays and the anniversaries of his birth and death will be particularly difficult).

• If you haven't yet called and a long time has gone by, tell me you are sorry, that you just haven't known what to say, but don't say you've been too busy! This has been an extremely large event in my life and it hurts to hear it has been so low on your priority list that you couldn't spare a 5- or 10-minute call.

• If you invite me for lunch in the midst of my grief, expect to talk about my loss. It's all I am thinking about anyway and I need to talk it out; small talk neither interests nor helps me now.

• Don't change the subject if I should start crying. Tears (and talking about it) are the healthiest way for me to release this intense emotion.

• Telling me that So-and-So's situation must have been harder to bear won't make mine easier. It only makes me feel you don't understand or can't acknowledge the extent of my pain.

• Don't expect that because "He is in the presence of the Lord" that is all that should matter (i.e. that I should not be hurting). I do believe he is, and I'm thankful for that, but my arms ache to hold him here and I miss him so.

• Now is not the time to tell me all about your own birth experiences – it reminds me painfully that you came home with a live baby and I didn't.

• Telling me I must be a very special person that God would send me such a heavy burden and that "God's Will is best" implies that God purposely did this. I believe His Will is best, too, but I don't believe everything that happens (including my baby's death or anyone being killed by a drunk driver, for instance) is God's Will.

• Don't remind me that I'm so lucky to have other kids – I am and I know it, but my pain is excruciating for THIS baby and the others don't take that away.

• No matter how bad I look, please don't say, "You look terrible." I feel like a total failure right now and I don't need to hear that I look awful too.

• Don't say, "I'm so glad you didn't get to hold him or nurse him." I am in agony because I didn't get to do those things. My arms ache to hold him and my breasts are full of milk meant for him, and the feelings of deprivation and missing my baby are so intense I can't imagine you'd believe it is easier for me this way.

• Don't devalue my baby ("Oh well, better luck next time," etc.) – to me he was a very special, unique person and there is no way he can ever be replaced. (Besides, you don't know if there ever will be a next time – I don't either and that is a pain all its own.)

• Don't say, "I know how you feel, I lost my mother ..." It is not the same. We all expect our parents to die one day after they have lived their lives, but I am intensely grieving for all the might-have-beens of my baby's life.

• When you ask my husband how I am doing don't forget to ask him how he's doing too. He also lost a son he was eagerly awaiting and if you ignore his hurt it says to him that his pain shouldn't exist or doesn't matter.

• Don't say, "You'd try again?" like I must be crazy. (If you had my history you might not want to face menopause without doing everything you could to change it either.)

• If I snap at you for saying any of the above (or anything else), please forgive me and try to understand it came from my intense pain. (Your dog might bite you when you try to pick him up at the side of the road after he's been hit by a car – that wouldn't mean he hates you or is ungrateful, just that he's been hurt and your touch, well-intentioned though it be, has added more pain.)

• Hug me; tell me you care and that you're sorry this happened.

• Be available to me often if you can and let me talk and cry without judging me. Saying, "Don't be angry" is like saying, "Don't be thirsty" – my feelings are part of a normal grief response and I will work through them quicker and easier if you aren't judgmental.

• Just love me and I will always remember you as a true friend.

"Homesick," song lyrics

By MercyMe, an American contemporary Christian band

You're in a better place, I've heard a thousand times
And at least a thousand times I've rejoiced for you
But the reason why I'm broken, the reason why I cry
Is how long must I wait to be with you

I close my eyes and I see your face
If home's where my heart is then I'm out of place
Lord, won't you give me strength to make it through
somehow
I've never been more homesick than now

Help me Lord cause I don't understand your ways
The reason why I wonder if I'll ever know
But, even if you showed me, the hurt would be the same
Cause I'm still here so far away from home

I close my eyes and I see your face
If home's where my heart is then I'm out of place
Lord, won't you give me strength to make it through
somehow
I've never been more homesick than now

In Christ, there are no goodbyes
And in Christ, there is no end
So I'll hold onto Jesus with all that I have
To see you again
To see you again

And I close my eyes and I see your face
If home's where my heart is then I'm out of place

(continued next page)

Lord, won't you give me strength to make it through somehow
Won't you give me strength to make it through somehow
Won't you give me strength to make it through somehow

I've never been more homesick than now

Contact the Bellephants

If you would like to reach Angie and Cecil Bellephant, you can contact them through the following e-mail address:

titusbellephant@yahoo.com